AN ADDENDUM TO
KING'S AND
SOME KING'S MEN
LONDON

OXFORD MEDICAL PUBLICATIONS

AN ADDENDUM TO

KING'S AND SOME KING'S MEN

(LONDON)

BEING AN ADDED RECORD OF
KING'S COLLEGE HOSPITAL AND OF
KING'S COLLEGE HOSPITAL MEDICAL SCHOOL
TO 5 JULY 1948

By

H. WILLOUGHBY LYLE, M.D., F.R.C.S.

Fellow of King's College, London
Dean Emeritus of King's College Hospital Medical School
Consulting Ophthalmic Surgeon to King's College Hospital
and Consulting Surgeon to the Royal Eye Hospital
London

GEOFFREY CUMBERLEGE
OXFORD UNIVERSITY PRESS
LONDON   NEW YORK   TORONTO
1950

Oxford University Press, Amen House, London E.C. 4

GLASGOW NEW YORK TORONTO MELBOURNE WELLINGTON
BOMBAY CALCUTTA MADRAS CAPE TOWN

Geoffrey Cumberlege, Publisher to the University

PRINTED IN GREAT BRITAIN

PREFACE

As the existence of King's College Hospital as a London Voluntary Teaching Hospital has terminated in that it has become nationalized and has been taken over by the Ministry of National Health and has become part of the National Hospital Service, and as King's College Hospital Medical School has become a Body Corporate under the name of King's College Hospital Medical School (University of London), it is evident that it is the duty of a King's man to bring the history of the Hospital and the Medical School up to the date of the 'appointed day' July 5, 1948, and to record the names of many who, by devotion to their Hospital and Medical School, have done much to enhance the reputation of both.

Many of the events recorded in the history of King's have been set out in the volume *King's and Some King's Men, London,* which covers the period from 1829, when King's College, London, was founded by Royal Charter, to the year 1934.

In writing this 'Addendum' to *King's and Some King's Men, London,* the opportunity has been taken to include some relevant matter which has not appeared in the original work, and to extend an account of the Hospital and Medical School to the date of the 'appointed day'.

The reputation of a Hospital with its Medical School is built up by those who have striven in its interest and for its advancement, so that particular reference is made in chronological order to the names of some of those members of the Medical Staff who have devotedly served both institutions:

ROBERT BENTLEY TODD and SIR WILLIAM FERGUSSON[1];

RICHARD PARTRIDGE[1] and SIR WILLIAM BOWMAN;

WILLIAM A. GUY and SIR GEORGE JOHNSON;

LIONEL S. BEALE and JOHN WOOD;

WILLIAM S. PLAYFAIR and SIR DAVID FERRIER;

JOHN CURNOW and URBAN PRITCHARD;

LORD LISTER and SIR W. WATSON CHEYNE[1];

SIR JOHN PHILLIPS and ALBERT CARLESS;

FREDERIC F. BURGHARD and SIR G. LENTHAL CHEATLE;

SIR RAYMOND H. P. CRAWFURD and ARTHUR H. CHEATLE;

L. VERNON CARGILL and SIR FREDERIC STILL;

SIR ST. CLAIR THOMSON and HUGH J. M. PLAYFAIR;

SIR J. CHARLTON BRISCOE and T. PERCY LEGG;

ARTHUR EDMUNDS and A. C. DOUGLAS FIRTH.

[1] Richard Partridge became President of the Royal College of Surgeons in 1866, Sir William Fergusson in 1870, and Sir Watson Cheyne in 1914.

The reputation of the Nursing Institution of King's has been made
and increased by those who have occupied the responsible post of
Sister Matron, namely, Miss Katharine Monk, Miss Elsie M. Ray,
Miss M. A. Willcox, and Miss M. K. Blyde.

Many members of the Committee of Management have done a
great deal to enhance the usefulness of the Hospital. In this connexion
the members of two well-known families are outstanding—the Twinings and the Smiths (later the Hambledens). Richard Twining of the
Strand and W. H. Smith, Jnr., also of the Strand were strong financial
supporters of King's College when it was founded in 1829. Mention
is also made of Robert Cheere, Thomas Godfrey Sambrooke, and
Edward Wigram, all of whom did much for King's.

It must be placed on record that women students in limited numbers
have been admitted to the Medical School and Hospital since the
year 1918; they, with the men students, have taken their full share
in promoting the interests of both Institutions.

In 1920 ladies became appointed members of the Committee of
Management and served on some of the sub-committees. Those who
served for many years and rendered devoted service to King's are
the Dowager Viscountess Hambleden, the Hon. Mrs. Charles Tufton,
and the Hon. Mrs. Anthony Henley. In the year 1937, one hundred
years after Queen Victoria came to the Throne, H.R.H. the Duchess
of Gloucester became the first lady to be elected President of King's
College Hospital.

An opportunity is taken to express my grateful thanks to Mr.
Sydney T. Shovelton, the former Secretary of King's College, London,
in allowing me the use of many calendars of the College; to Dr. E.
Bellis Clayton for his assistance in the preparation of the section which
deals with the Physical Treatment Department; to Miss J. Justice for
her help in writing the section on the Almoner's Department; to the
Rev. Sidney C. Ranner, the previous Secretary of the Medical School,
for his kindness in supervising lists referring to the department in
which he was so long engaged; to Sir Thomas Creed, K.C., the
Secretary of the University of London King's College; to Mr. W. F.
Gunn, the Secretary of the Medical School; to Mr. S. W. Barnes, the
House Governor and Secretary of King's College Hospital; and lastly
to my friend and colleague Dr. John A. Drake, for the great care he
expended in reading and correcting the typed folios and manuscript,
also to my son Dr. T. Keith Lyle, for his many useful suggestions and
his valuable assistance in correcting the proof sheets.

H. WILLOUGHBY LYLE

London 1950

CONTENTS

CONTENTS

LIST OF PLATES

KING'S COLLEGE HOSPITAL, PORTUGAL STREET, LINCOLN'S INN FIELDS. THE LISTERIAN PERIOD. THE CHURCH OF ST. CLEMENT DANES. THE TWININGS. STRAND HOUSE. CENTENARY TABLET. SOME KING'S MEN

THE Medical Department of King's College, London, was established in 1831, but at that time there was no hospital connected with the College. In 1839 the first King's College Hospital was founded and opened in 1840 in the old St. Clement Danes Workhouse in Portugal Street, close to Lincoln's Inn Fields.

It was a fundamental principle of the newly acquired Hospital that its honorary medical officers should be professors and teachers in the Medical Department of King's College so that they would have the opportunity of demonstrating in the wards the theories they enunciated in the lecture-theatre and classrooms of the College. It was also laid down by the Council of King's College that the Hospital was a public hospital for the relief of poor, sick, and infirm persons and to it the students in the Medical Department of King's College should, under proper regulations, for ever have access.

At the time when the first King's College Hospital was opened in 1840, and the second King's College Hospital built on the site of the first one and opened for the reception of patients in 1861, there were in the immediate vicinity Clare Market, Clare Street, Stanhope Street, Holles Street, Houghton Street, Gilbert Street, and Bear Yard—all densely populated; in fact, the position of the Hospital was in one of the poorest and most crowded districts in London. Eventually the Hospital became filled with some of the worst and most varied types of disease.

In order that the kind of persons who attended the Out-Patients' Department and of many of those who became in-patients at the Hospital in its earliest days may be readily understood, a brief account of some part of the immediate vicinity of the Hospital is set out.

Between the years 1865 and 1870 about eight acres of land, situated south-east of the Hospital and immediately west of Temple Bar, which divided Fleet Street (City) from the Strand, were cleared to make way for the new Courts of Justice, opened in 1882.

About thirty close, foul, and filthy courts, yards, lanes, and alleys were swept away to make room for the Law Courts. Four hundred houses were pulled down and over four thousand persons were turned out of their homes and eventually made their way into Clare Market, Drury Lane, and Seven Dials, situated immediately west of the Hospital.

Amongst the buildings in the Strand in the immediate vicinity of Temple Bar were 'The Old Fish Shop' carried on by Short and Son, established in the reign of King Henry VIII, which later passed into the hands of Messrs. Reeves and Turner, second-hand booksellers, also the house of Messrs. Holloway, the wholesale manufacturers of pills, and the offices of the *Daily Telegraph*, the first of the penny daily papers. These buildings stood nearly opposite Messrs. Twining's Bank and business premises, situated on the south side of the Strand.

The area which was cleared for the Courts of Justice lay between Carey Street on the north, Pickett Street (see Pl. 1) and the Strand on the south, Bell Yard on the east, and St. Clement's Lane on the west.

The building of the Law Courts commenced in 1874 at the north-east corner between Carey Street and Bell Yard.

Amongst the areas which were demolished was Shire Lane (Shere Lane), a thoroughfare for foot-passengers only, a meeting-place of beggars and thieves. As early as the reign of James I this lane was known as 'Rogues Lane', but in 1845 the name was changed to that of Upper, Middle, and Lower Serles Place.

Another area of ill repute and a real colony of thieves was Ship Yard, adjoining Shire Lane. Ship Yard contained the Ship Inn, a house established in honour of Sir Francis Drake. It is said that executions at Newgate seldom occurred without someone from Ship Yard being amongst the number. At the end house of the block of buildings in Ship Yard was a den known as the 'Smashing Lumber', used for the manufacture of counterfeit coin.

Other courts and alleys of unwholesome atmosphere which were demolished to make way for the Courts of Justice were Bailey's Court, Swan Court, Star Court, White Hart Court, Lock Alley, Windmill Court, Hemlock Court, Great and Little Horseshoe Court, Plough Court, Yeates Court, Chair Court, Little Shere Lane leading from Ship Yard, and Old Boswell Court, once the abode of the widow of Sir Walter Raleigh, and the abode of Sir Edward Lyttleton, Lord Chief Justice of England in 1639.

Another court which was demolished in 1865 was New Boswell Court; at the side of a flight of steps leading to this court in former days there was a night-watchman's box, the last box of the 'Charlies'; this box was elevated from the pavement during day-time.

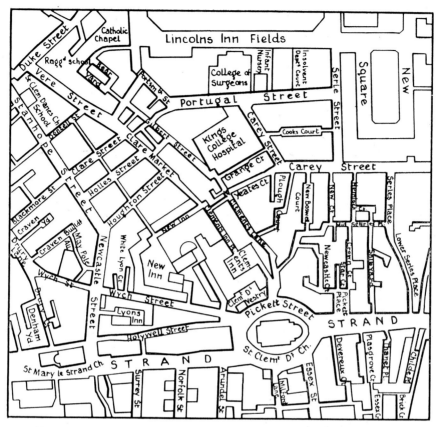

MAP OF THE IMMEDIATE VICINITY OF THE FIRST KING'S COLLEGE
HOSPITAL, PORTUGAL STREET, LINCOLN'S INN FIELDS

THE VICTORIA WARD, SIR JOSEPH LISTER SEATED IN THE CENTRE, 1891

Up to the year 1829 no 'Charlies' or night-watchmen dared to enter any of these areas of such bad repute, but after the organization of the new police force by Sir Robert Peel in that year, many of these dens gradually came under the observation of the police and then were slowly abolished.

The courts and alleys in the immediate vicinity of the Hospital were thickly populated slums. It is said that in Yeates Court, which was situated behind the Hospital, there were 6 small houses tenanted by 48 families and there were besides adults some 158 children.

In early days, immediately northwards of St. Clement Danes was a narrow passage, flanked by squalid-looking buildings mostly built in Queen Elizabeth's time, called Butchers Row from having served as slaughter-houses. This passage was frequently referred to as the 'Straits of St. Clements'. In one of these houses was born in 1787 Dr. Andrew Reed, the founder of Reedham, a home for fatherless children at Clapton, and the Asylum at Earlswood, Surrey. In this Row the Gunpowder Plot was concocted by Robert Catesby, Thomas Percy, Christopher and John Wright, Thomas and Robert Winter, and Guy Fawkes in 1605. In this unsavoury area there was a well-known public-house—'The Bear and Harrow'—situated at the extreme entrance to 'Bear and Harrow Court'. About the year 1803 the whole street was demolished by Alderman Pickett and a wider street constructed, which was known as Pickett Street (see Pl. 1).

Later, the name of the street was dropped and it became part of the east portion of the Strand. From Pickett Street St. Clement's Lane bore off to the back of King's College Hospital, merging into Gilbert Street and Gilbert Passage.

THE LISTERIAN PERIOD

1877–93

When Professor Joseph Lister came to King's in 1877 the larger portion of the unsavoury courts and alleys just described had disappeared and the new Courts of Justice were in process of erection.

Joseph Lister brought his antiseptic system to King's; he established it and eventually his dictum also, namely: 'The occurrence of suppuration in a wound made by a surgeon through unbroken skin denotes to me defect in his antiseptic precautions.'

The most striking features in Lister's operative work were his extreme care, his gentleness, and his deliberation, together with his efforts to diminish loss of blood.

The accompanying picture (Pl. 2), taken in 1891, two years before

Sir Joseph Lister retired from the active staff of King's College Hospital, represents the surgical ward to which his male cases were admitted.

In April 1895 Sir Joseph Lister was received by the Prince of Wales at Marlborough House and presented by His Royal Highness with the Albert Medal of the Society of Arts, which had been awarded to him in recognition of his application of antiseptic methods to practical surgery.

On March 29, 1897, the portrait of Lord Lister, P.R.S., painted for the subscribers by W. W. Ouless, R.A., was presented to the Royal College of Surgeons of England and received on behalf of the College by the President, Sir William MacCormac.

Lister and his former pupils

On May 26, 1897, Lord Lister was entertained at dinner by his former house surgeons, clinical clerks, and dressers at the Café Royal, London. Of his eight surviving house surgeons at Glasgow seven were present. Five of those who acted in a similar capacity at Edinburgh attended, and eighteen of his house surgeons at King's were present. The Chairman was Professor Joseph Coats of Glasgow, who had been one of his dressers at the Royal Infirmary. During the evening R. Hamilton Ramsay of Torquay presented to Lister an album containing an address and 130 signatures of those present; the Rev. J. E. London, M.R.C.S., also presented an address from the native practitioners of British Guiana.

Sir Michael Foster's epigram on the life of Lister was:

'In early life Lister belonged to a Society the members of which call all men Friends, and now in turn, because of his beneficence and service to mankind all men the world over call him Friend.'

THE CHURCH OF ST. CLEMENT DANES

The Old King's College Hospital was situated in the parish of St. Clement Danes Church in the Strand, west of Temple Bar. The original church, dedicated to St. Clement, the patron saint of felt-workers and of sailors, was built by Danes probably during the reign of Canute (A.D. 1017–36). The fabric which stood a little to the south of the ancient church of St. Clement, which occupied part of the old churchyard, was built by Edward Pearce, under the direction of Sir Christopher Wren, in 1682; the tower and steeple were added in 1719 and the building was repaired and completely restored in 1839, the year that the first King's College Hospital was incepted. It is believed that the church covered the grave of Harold I (Harefoot), the son and successor of Canute on the English throne. He reigned over London and the country north of the Thames from 1036 to 1040, when he died. The church eventually became the parish church of Danes and also of Australians in London.

In the north gallery of the church and situated immediately behind the pulpit was the pew, indicated by a brass plate, placed there in 1851, originally occupied by Dr. Samuel Johnson (1709–84). The rector, The Rev. W. Pennington-Bickford, founded the Johnson Society of London in 1929.

On March 3, 1872, services were held in St. Clement Danes Church as a thanksgiving for the restoration to health of H.R.H. The Prince of Wales. Funds raised at these services were named the Albert Edward Fund, and in 1875 were utilized at King's College Hospital for Samaritan purposes.

In 1894 William Frederick Danvers Smith, later the second Viscount Hambleden (see *King's*, p. 383), was married to Lady Esther Gore, the third daughter of the fifth Earl of Arran, at St. Clement Danes.

In 1913, when King's College Hospital was removed to Denmark Hill and the old Hospital demolished, Viscount Hambleden had the tombstone to Honest Joe Miller (see *King's*, p. 32), which was previously beneath the main staircase of the Hospital, removed, and presented to the Rev. W. Pennington-Bickford, Rector of St. Clement Danes. It was then placed on the wall of the stairway leading to the north gallery of that church.

In March 1923 a memorial service was held in the church to the memory of Dr. Norman Dalton (see *King's*, p. 395), Consulting Physician to King's, who in his earlier days had been a resident in the parish of St. Clement Danes.

On April 11, 1930, Arthur Wallis Kendall, who later became Assistant-Surgeon and Vice-Dean at K.C.H., was married to Miss Verna Hackett, daughter of the late Sir John Winthrop Hackett, K.C.M.G., of Western Australia, at St. Clement Danes. On that occasion oranges and lemons constituted the main feature of the decorations in the church. The rector had restored the bells of St. Clements, and instituted the Annual Children's Festival of Oranges and Lemons in 1919.

On St. Luke's Day, October 18, 1934, a Commemoration Service of Thanksgiving, conducted by the Archbishop of Canterbury, upon the twenty-first anniversary of the opening of K.C.H. and the Medical School on Denmark Hill, was held at St. Clement Danes Church (see *King's*, p. 379).

The family of Twining has been closely connected with the parish of St. Clement Danes for over 200 years; in the year 1893 Samuel Harvey Twining (1820–1900) was senior churchwarden (see pp. 7, 8) and later Herbert H. Twining (see p. 8) became churchwarden.

In the south aisle of the church there were two stained-glass windows which were of particular interest to King's people. One, 'I am the Bread of Life', Christ with the Faithful at Holy Communion, was the Hon. W. F. D. Smith's and Lady Esther Gore's Marriage Window, and the other, 'I am the Good Shepherd', was the W. H. Smith Memorial Window (see p. 19).

The Church of St. Clement Danes was badly damaged during the War (1939–45) and finally destroyed by enemy action on the night of September 24–5, 1940. In St. Clement's Lane, opposite the north side of the church, was the Holy Well of St. Clement. Later this well appears to have become covered by a pump, and eventually filled in when the Law Courts were built. It was supposed that this well supplied the old Roman Bath in Strand Lane (see *King's*, p. 35), but that appears to be a mistake. The water which supplied the bath springs up out of the London clay below what used to be known as Holywell Street, once the headquarters of sellers of old books, and later called 'Booksellers' Row'; Holywell Street was named after the Holy Well of St. Clement. The old Roman Bath in Strand Lane was secured by the Rev. Pennington-Bickford in 1922 and opened to the public.

The Rev. Pennington-Bickford, born in 1874, was rector of St. Clement Danes for thirty-one years; he died in 1941, soon after his church had been destroyed by enemy action.

THE TWININGS

Ever since the foundation of King's College, London, in 1828, and of King's College Hospital in 1839, members of the Twining family of the Strand have taken a practical interest in both institutions.

Richard Twining II (1771–1859), his younger brothers George Twining (1778–1850) and John Aldred Twining (1785–1855), and his son Richard Twining III (1807–1906) were all 'Donors of the first class' to King's College, London (see *King's*, p. 35). In 1850 the Twinings resigned their pecuniary rights as shareholders in the College, but retained their privileges as Donors.

Richard Twining II, F.R.S., son of Richard Twining I (1749–1824), became a member of the Council of King's College in 1851 and was styled 'The Peace-Maker' by the Rev. Dr. Jelf, Principal of the College. He was appointed a member of the first Committee of

THE OPERATING THEATRE, KING'S COLLEGE HOSPITAL, IN WHICH SIR JOSEPH LISTER
USED TO OPERATE AND DELIVER HIS CLINICAL LECTURES
It shows the door leading to the surgeons' room
From left to right: Theatre Sister, Theatre Staff Nurse, E. W. Webster, Assistant Theatre Porter, and
George Till, Theatre Porter

Management of King's College Hospital in 1839 (see *King's*, p. 38). He and his brother George Twining became Governors of the Hospital in 1842. When the new wing of the Hospital was built in 1852, his family decided, as a suitable memorial for his unremitting interest in the affairs of King's College and the Hospital, to build and to endow a ward to be named after him.

The Twining Ward contained his portrait and a marble bust in order to keep alive his memory and his long connexion with King's. In 1916 a sum of money was bequeathed by the will of Samuel Twining and constituted the 'Samuel Twining Fund' for the support of the Twining Ward.

Amongst Richard Twining's (II) eight children were Richard Twining III (who was Treasurer of King's College Hospital from 1886 to 1897) and Louisa Twining, the youngest.

Miss Louisa Twining (1820–1912), the Poor Law and workhouse reformer, was born at 34 Norfolk Street, Strand. For over sixty years she devoted herself to ameliorating the conditions of the workhouse system and particularly those of workhouse infirmaries. She commenced her Poor Law work in 1848 and began her visits to the poor of St. Clement Danes parish; in 1853 she paid her first visit to the new workhouse of St. Clement Danes, Strand. She conceived the idea that women might do much for the women and children in the workhouses, which at that time were governed by male guardians. One result of her efforts was the separation of Union workhouses from infirmaries.

She first met Miss Florence Nightingale at the 'Home' in Chandos Street, London, in 1854, a short time before the Crimean War brought Miss Nightingale into public notice (see *King's*, p. 54). It was mainly due to the power and personality of Florence Nightingale that there has arisen a great profession of hospital-trained nurses.

In 1865 the *Lancet* Commission, of which Dr. Francis Edmund Anstie (see *King's*, p. 72), Dr. Carr, and Mr. Ernest Hart were members, was appointed to make an inquiry into workhouse administration, and did much to facilitate her work (see *King's*, p. 73).

Miss Twining was considerably helped in her social work by Miss Florence Nightingale, Miss Mary Carpenter of Red Lodge, Bristol, Miss Selwyn, sister of the Bishop of New Zealand, Sir William Bowman (see *King's*, p. 110), and William Fairlie Clarke, at that time Surgical Registrar at King's (see *King's*, pp. 94 and 438).

Miss Twining published her *Recollections of Life and Work* in 1893, and on page 163 we read: 'I was present at the laying of the first stone [of the new wing] of King's College Hospital [in 1852] which was to replace the old building, formerly the parish workhouse [of St. Clement Danes]. Some years later, in 1857, I undertook to assist in collecting the sum of £10,000 towards the completion of this object, and this was accomplished, by the help of an influential committee, in due time.' (See *King's*, p. 55.) She was Secretary of the Ladies' Appeal Committee appointed in 1857.

In 1912 Miss Twining endowed a bed in the Twining Ward; it is named the Louisa Twining Bed.

Throughout her life she worked hard and unremittingly for the admission of women to many public offices of usefulness, and believed that 'in the "Communion of Labour" and the sharing of work by men and women, the best interests of both could be developed and forwarded'.

Her last words of advice to social workers were 'Patience, Perseverance and Faith'. She died in 1912, aged 91.

HERBERT HAYNES TWINING (1849–1935), J.P.

Herbert H. Twining was a direct descendant of Thomas Twining (1675–1741), who founded the well-known tea firm in 1706.

He was born in 1849 and was the eldest son of Samuel Harvey Twining (1820–1900), banker and tea merchant of the Strand, grandson of John Aldred Twining (1785–1855) and a first cousin of Miss Louisa Twining.

Herbert H. Twining was educated at Elstree School and at Harrow, and in 1869 he followed his father in the family bank and tea business of R. Twining & Co., Ltd., at 216 Strand.

On the amalgamation of Twining's Bank with Lloyds in 1892, he became joint-manager of Lloyds Bank, Strand.

He was closely interested in the parish of St. Clement Danes in which he was born. He was at one time an overseer and churchwarden of the parish, also a governor and manager of St. Clement Danes' Schools. He was also a trustee of the Craven Charity (see Craven Ward, *King's*, p. 92). He was present at the Thanksgiving Service held in 1934 in St. Clement Danes (see p. 5), the church in which he had been baptized.

Herbert H. Twining was a Governor of King's College Hospital for forty years. He joined the Committee of Management in 1894 and in 1913 he became Honorary Treasurer of the Hospital in succession to Charles Awdry; he remained Treasurer until 1921, when he retired from that office and was elected a Vice-President of the Hospital.

He was succeeded on the Committee of Management at King's by his son Temple Craufurd Twining, elected in 1929.

STRAND HOUSE

King's College Hospital in Portugal Street, Lincoln's Inn Fields, was finally closed on July 31, 1913, and the site was purchased by the firm of W. H. Smith & Son. The building was rapidly demolished by the end of September, and upon the site of the Hospital, which once had been the old workhouse of St. Clement Danes' parish, also on an adjacent burial-ground belonging to the parish of St. Clement Danes, and on the site of the Grange public house with its once picturesque yard, was placed the fine building now known as Strand House.

THE UNVEILING OF THE CENTENARY TABLET

As a fitting climax to the work of King's College Hospital during the past hundred years, and also to the close association of the firm of Messrs. W. H. Smith & Son with the Hospital during that period, on April 17, 1940, the Dowager Viscountess Hambleden unveiled the Centenary Tablet on the outside wall of Strand House, the head offices of W. H. Smith & Son in Portugal Street.

The tablet is inscribed:

> 'This tablet records the grateful
> thanks of King's College Hospital,
> which stood upon this site from 1839
> to 1913, to the firm and staff of
> W. H. Smith and Son for their generous
> and unfailing support during the 100
> years of its existence.
> 1939'

The unveiling was preceded by an address by Sir Frederic Still, in which he briefly outlined the history of the Hospital from 1839 to 1913, when it was moved from its site in Portugal Street to Denmark Hill.

He referred to the family of the Smiths who had been active supporters of the Hospital since 1842, and especially to the Hon. W. F. D. Smith (later second Viscount Hambleden), who by his counsel and benefactions solved the major difficulties of the Committee of Management and set the Hospital on its way to a wider sphere of usefulness at Denmark Hill.

Amongst a large gathering of friends of King's there were present Viscount and Viscountess Hambleden, the Marquess of Salisbury, Mr. A. D. Power (Vice-President of the Hospital), the Hon. George Colville (Vice-Chairman), Sir Herbert E. Morgan (Chairman of the Centenary Executive Committee), the Rev. Cyril Eastaugh

(Chaplain), the Rev. W. Pennington-Bickford (Rector of St. Clement Danes), Sir St. Clair Thomson, L. Vernon Cargill, and H. Willoughby Lyle, also Dr. C. D. Webb and Mr. J. F. Hales (representing King's College), H. E. Cheffings and E. W. Stowe (formerly officials of the hospital office), Miss M. A. Willcox (formerly Sister Matron), Miss M. K. Blyde (Sister Matron), Miss G. L. Buffard (Assistant Matron), Miss M. R. Walker (Matron of the Royal Manchester Children's Hospital), Mrs. M. Purkis, Miss Mary A. Peddie, Miss Marjorie Greener, and Emma A. Soton.

SOME KING'S MEN OF OLD K.C.H.

WILLIAM FAIRLIE CLARKE (1833–1884), M.A., M.B. OXON. (1862), M.D. (1876), F.R.C.S. (1863).

Fairlie Clarke was educated at Rugby. He entered Christ Church, Oxford, in 1852 and graduated B.A. in 1856. He was intended for the Bar and went to Edinburgh to study Medical Jurisprudence under Dr. Littlejohn. He decided, however, to take up Medicine and entered the Medical Department of King's College in 1858. He joined the Medical Society of King's College in 1859 and was awarded the Society's Prize for his essay on Cancer in 1861. He passed the M.R.C.S. in 1862. In 1863 he was the first Surgical Registrar to be appointed at K.C.H., and in 1864 was succeeded by Edward Bellamy. He was also Demonstrator of Anatomy at King's College, Assistant Surgeon at the West London Hospital, and Assistant Surgeon at Charing Cross Hospital from 1871 to 1877; he then left London to practise at Southborough, near Tunbridge Wells, where a drinking-fountain commemorates his good work amongst the poor. He died at Bonchurch, Isle of Wight, on May 8, 1884.

When Fairlie Clarke came to King's he was introduced to Miss Louisa Twining by his brother Canon Erskine Clarke. He volunteered to help her in the Sunday afternoon services which she had organized at the Strand Union Workhouse (see p. 7). He was usually accompanied by his friend Charles P. Bosanquet, a barrister who subsequently became the first Honorary Secretary of the Charity Organization Society.

Fairlie Clarke was an influential member of the Medical Prayer Union. In London his memory is perpetuated by the 'Fairlie Clarke Conversazione', an annual meeting of medical students begun by himself and continued by the Medical Missionary Society.

He was particularly interested in Medical Missions and Temperance questions. He wrote on the Medical Charities of London, the overcrowding of the out-patient departments of hospitals, and on Provident dispensaries.

He published *A Manual of the Practice of Surgery* (1865) and a *Treatise on the Diseases of the Tongue* (1873).

KENNETH COMYN, M.D. CANTAB. (1913), D.P.H. (1921), COLONEL, R.A.M.C.

Kenneth Comyn was educated at Cambridge and at King's. He obtained the M.R.C.S., L.R.C.P. in 1909, taking the M.B., B.Ch. in 1910. He then joined the R.A.M.C. and in 1921 obtained the D.P.H. and the D.T.M. of Cambridge and of the Royal College of Surgeons.

For a time he was Assistant Director of Hygiene to the Eastern Command and later he became Deputy Assistant Director of Hygiene of the Lucknow and Presidency Assam Districts.

Comyn is the author of *Infective Gastroenteritis in Children* and *Anti-Malaria Work at Moascar*, Egypt.

ANDREW CAREY McALLISTER, M.B., B.S. LOND. (1914), F.R.C.S. (1925), F.R.C.O.G. (1936).

Andrew McAllister entered the Medical Department of King's College, London, in 1905. He gained class prizes and passed the M.R.C.S., L.R.C.P. in 1912. He held the appointments of House Surgeon, Senior House Accoucheur, and House Physician for Children, and Aural House Surgeon at K.C.H.

In 1914 he was appointed Obstetric Registrar, but during the War (1914–18) he obtained a commission in the Royal Navy. He returned to King's in 1919 and was appointed Obstetric and Gynaecological Registrar and Tutor, an office which he filled with distinction until 1927. He became a Foundation Member of the College of Obstetricians and Gynaecologists in 1929.

In 1926 he was appointed Assistant Obstetric and Gynaecological Surgeon to Queen Mary's Hospital and full Surgeon in 1931.

In 1927 he became Assistant Surgeon to the Samaritan Free Hospital for Women and Surgeon in 1936. In 1927 he was also appointed Assistant Gynaecological Surgeon at the Royal Waterloo Hospital for Women, becoming full Surgeon in 1932.

During the time that Andrew McAllister was at King's he took a great interest in the athletic sports and in the Rugby Football Club, of which he became Treasurer.

For some years he has been Secretary of King's College Hospital Lodge (see *King's*, p. 484). He has written *Albuminuria and Eclampsia* and *Vomiting in Pregnancy*.

EDGAR WILLIAM MATTHEWS (b. 1880), T.D. (1935), M.B., B.S. Lond (1909), D.P.H. (1920).

Edgar Matthews was educated at Kingston Grammar School and in the Medical Department of King's College, London, which he entered in 1899. He joined the Hospital Medical School in 1903 and obtained the M.R.C.S., L.R.C.P. in 1906. He was House Physician and later House Surgeon. When Edgar Matthews joined King's he became a member of No. 1 Company of the Volunteer Medical Staff Corps. In 1906 he, with Harold Wiltshire, constituted the first pair of the Tennis Six which represented King's in the Junior Lawn Tennis Cup (see p. 169), and in 1907 he raised the first K.C.H. Hockey Team to play in the Inter-Hospitals Cup Competition (see p. 170). He was a member of the United Hospitals Hockey Team; he also played for Surrey.

After leaving King's in 1908, he became a medical companion and for a year travelled in the Argentine, Chile, Brazil, the United States of America, in Italy, Greece, Turkey, and in Egypt. During the War (1914–18) he was a member of the 3rd Home Counties Field Ambulance R.A.M.C., and served in England and in France; later he became Major Commanding the Medical Division of a Military Hospital in Chatham.

In 1919 Edgar Matthews was appointed School Medical Officer at Kingston-on-Thames and in 1921 he became Medical Officer for that district. In 1935 he retired from the Territorial Army with the rank of Lt.-Col. R.A.M.C., T. In 1939, under the National Service Act, he was appointed a member of the Brighton Medical Board.

FREDERICK CHARLES SPRAWSON (1872–1938), M.B. Lond. (1897), F.R.C.S. (1897), A.K.C. (1895).

Frederick Sprawson was the eldest of four brothers, all of whom entered the medical profession (see *King's*, p. 321). He went to King's College School in 1883 and joined the Medical Department of King's College in 1888. He was a surgical dresser under Sir Joseph Lister, obtained the M.R.C.S., L.R.C.P. in 1894, and was appointed House Surgeon. During the time he was at King's he did the photographic illustrations for the first edition of *Rose and Carless*.

For many years Frederick Sprawson had a consulting ophthalmic and general surgical practice in Blackpool. He was Consulting Surgeon to the Lytham and Fleetwood Hospitals and Surgeon to the Victoria Hospital, Blackpool.

During the War (1914–18) he volunteered for service, and on the way to Salonika the ship *Ivernia*, in which he was travelling, was torpedoed in the Mediterranean and he narrowly escaped death from drowning. His chief concern at the time appeared to have been the loss of his cases of surgical instruments.

He retired from practice in 1931 and went to live in Hayling Island, where he died.

CHARLES JOHN WILLMER TATHAM (1861–1936), O.B.E., COLONEL, R.A.M.C.

Charles Tatham was educated at King's College, Cambridge, King's College, London, and at King's College Hospital.

He obtained the M.R.C.S. in 1883, the L.S.A. in 1884, and the D.P.H. in 1894.

He joined the R.A.M.C. in 1886. He had a gift for organization, and during the South African War (1899–1902) he was attached to the Naval Staff and directed the embarkation of some 66,000 invalid troops from the Cape.

During the War (1914–18) he was Assistant Director of Medical Services, Northern Command, and was awarded the O.B.E.

SIR WILLIAM TURNER THISELTON-DYER (1843–1928), C.M.G. (1882), C.I.E. (1892), K.C.M.G. (1899), M.A., D.Sc., LL.D., PH.D., F.R.S. (1880), F.K.C. (1886).

William Thiselton-Dyer received his early education at King's College School where he formed a friendship with Henry Trimen (see *King's*, p. 96) and with him began those botanical rambles which led later to the publication of their *Flora of Middlesex* (1869).

In 1861 he was awarded a Warneford Scholarship and entered the Medical Department of King's College, London, where Henry Trimen was already a student, and where he also came in contact with Charles James Lyall (the Indian administrator), who had been at King's College School and who was a student at King's College from 1861 to 1863.

Thiselton-Dyer joined the Medical Society of King's College in 1861 (see *King's*, p. 438). He obtained honours in Biology at the Preliminary Science Examination at the University of London in 1863 and was awarded the Leathes Prize at King's College. He obtained a studentship in Physical Science at Christ Church, Oxford, where he was awarded First Class in Natural Science in 1867. In the following year he was appointed Professor of Natural History at the Royal Agricultural College, Cirencester.

He was Professor of Botany in the Royal College of Science, Dublin, from 1870 to 1872 and at South Kensington and Chiswick from 1872 to 1875. In 1872 he was one of T. H. Huxley's demonstrators at the Royal School of Mines.

In 1875 he was appointed Assistant Director at the Royal Gardens at Kew under Joseph D. Hooker where he had to deal chiefly with colonial business. In this office he was a great success and eventually Mr. Joseph Chamberlain and Thiselton-Dyer became close friends, and when Mr. Chamberlain was at the Colonial Office (1895–1903) they worked together for the advancement of economic botany and colonial agriculture. In 1902 Thiselton-Dyer was appointed Botanical Adviser to the Secretary of State for the Colonies and held that office until 1906. On the retirement of Sir Joseph Dalton Hooker in 1885, Thiselton-Dyer was appointed Director of the Royal Botanical Gardens at Kew, an appointment which he held until 1905, when he retired. 'He really improved and beautified the gardens, enlarged the library and the herbarium building, initiated a forestry museum, and made the Jodrell Laboratory the best botanical laboratory in Europe.'

Thiselton-Dyer was a great administrator, a sound and an accomplished systematic botanist.

He was Vice-President of the Royal Society (1896–7). He wrote extensively and edited the English edition of Julius von Sachs's *Text-Book of Botany* (1875).

Thiselton-Dyer died at Winchcombe, Gloucestershire, on December 23, 1928.

HENRY TRIMEN (1843–1896), M.B. Lond. (1865), F.R.S. (1888).

Henry Trimen was educated at King's College School, where he formed a lasting friendship with William T. Thiselton-Dyer (see p. 13). He entered the Medical Department of King's College in 1860, where some of his fellow students were Michael Beverley (see *King's*, p. 73), A. Baird Seaman (see *King's*, p. 158), and Shephard T. Taylor (see *King's*, p. 163). At the M.B. examination in 1865 Trimen obtained honours in Medicine and Midwifery.

Trimen became Assistant in the Botanical Department of the British Museum in 1861 and was appointed Curator of the Anatomical Museum at King's College, London, in 1867. Two years later (1869) with W. T. Thiselton-Dyer he published the *Flora of Middlesex*. He was appointed Editor of the *Journal of Botany* in 1871, and in conjunction with Robert Bentley, who was Professor of Botany at King's College, London, from 1859 to 1887, he published *Medicinal Plants* (1875–80).

In 1879 Henry Trimen became Director of the Botanical Gardens at Peradeniya in Ceylon, where in 1880 he received from Thiselton-Dyer certain varieties of cacao from Trinidad, which flourished and are still under cultivation in Ceylon. He published a *Handbook of the Flora of Ceylon* (1893).

JAMES WHEATLEY (d. 1928), M.D. LOND. (1890), D.P.H. EDIN. (1891).

James Wheatley came to King's College, London, in 1881 when he was awarded a Clothworkers' Science Exhibition. In 1882 he won a Junior Scholarship; the other Junior Scholars of the year being Albert Carless and Albert Lindow.

At the Intermediate M.B. Lond. in 1884 he obtained First Class Honours and became Assistant Demonstrator of Anatomy at King's College. He qualified with the M.R.C.S. and L.S.A. in 1886 and was appointed House Physician; in the same year he joined the Medical Society of King's College.

In 1887 he passed the M.B. with honours in Medicine and later he also took the B.S. After leaving King's he became Medical Officer of Health and Medical Superintendent of the Fever and Small Pox Hospitals at Blackburn, and in 1901 he was appointed M.O.H. for the County of Shropshire.

Wheatley wrote on 'Influence of the Cotton Industry on the Health of Operatives'; 'Trade Mortality Statistics'; 'Dental Caries from a Public Health Standpoint' and 'Factors contributing to the Recent Decline in Infant Mortality'.

THEODORE HENRY WHITTINGTON, M.D. LOND. (1912), M.R.C.P. (1931), D.O.M.S. (1921).

Theodore Whittington entered the Medical Department of King's College, London, in October 1904, having been awarded a Warneford Entrance Scholarship; he also obtained the Warneford and other prizes. In 1909 he was awarded the Todd Prize for Clinical Medicine and passed the M.R.C.S., L.R.C.P. He was House Surgeon in 1910, and later in the year he became House Physician. During the time he was in residence at K.C.H. he acted as Ophthalmic House Surgeon.

In 1911 Whittington passed the M.B., B.S. and gained honours in Medicine. From 1911 to 1914 he was Clinical Assistant in the Ophthalmic Department at King's. From 1914 to 1917 he became Captain R.A.M.C., served abroad, and was mentioned in dispatches. In 1918 he was appointed Ophthalmologist to the General Military

Hospital, Colchester, and later to the 4th London General Hospital (K.C.H.) (see *King's*, p. 330).

After the War (1914–18) Whittington returned to assist in the work of the Ophthalmic Department at King's, in which, since 1930, he has been the Chief Assistant.

Whittington was in the Rugby Football Fifteen from 1904 to 1911 and was a member of the United Hospitals Rugby Football Committee in 1908. He was also Secretary of the Athletic Sports at K.C.L. in 1907 and 1908, when he represented the Medical Faculty of the College in the mile and in putting the weight. He was also Secretary of King's College Boxing Club when boxing took place in the Gymnasium in the basement of the College.

Theodore Whittington is Ophthalmic Surgeon to the Royal Waterloo Hospital and to the Sutton and Cheam Hospital; he is also Ophthalmic Physician to the Royal Eye Hospital.

He has written on 'Ocular Complications of Chronic Epidemic Encephalitis' and on other ophthalmic subjects.

CAMBERWELL. THE HAMBLEDENS. KING'S COLLEGE HOSPITAL AND KING'S COLLEGE HOSPITAL MEDICAL SCHOOL, DENMARK HILL.

CAMBERWELL

THIS southern Metropolitan borough of London was mentioned in the Domesday Book where it was referred to as Ca'brewelle. In various old records the district has been named Camwell, Camerwell, Cambwell, and in the middle of the eighteenth century it became Camberwell. The origin of the name is obscure, but it is said that there is an old British word *cam* which signifies 'crooked'. Three ancient wells appear to have been discovered in the parish and Dr. J. C. Lettsom, whose home was at Grove Hill, claimed to have in his grounds the identical well from which the parish of Camberwell derives its name.

The ancient parish church of Camberwell is named after St. Giles, who was the patron saint of cripples. Camberwell may perhaps indicate 'the well for the crooked', and it is possible that cripples formerly came to the district for the 'healing powers' of these wells.

It is certainly significant and of interest to record that in 1919 King's College Hospital opened an Orthopaedic Department for the inhabitants of Camberwell and surrounding neighbourhood, and in 1938 an Orthoptist was appointed in the Ophthalmic Department.

In 1809 Camberwell was described as a 'pleasant retreat for those citizens who have a taste for the country whilst their avocations daily call them to town' (Priscilla Wakefield).

The Metropolitan Borough of Camberwell has a total area of 4,480 acres. In 1801 the population was 7,059 and in 1931, 251,294; since that time the population has increased considerably.

Although King's College Hospital is situated in the parish of Lambeth, it was moved to the south-eastern district of London in 1912 in order to serve the vast population of Camberwell and surrounding district; hence there is a large amount of 'clinical material' available at the Hospital.

The most ancient part of the neighbourhood appears to be Camberwell Green. In bygone times it was the scene of an annual fair which was held in the month of August and usually lasted for three days. The fair was given up in 1855. A survival of this ancient fair took place in 1933, when a 'Brighter Camberwell Week' was organized by the Camberwell Green Tradesmen's Association in aid of the Hospital. The fair was held on the Medical School Sports Ground on Dog Kennel Hill and was visited on July 10 by Prince George, the Duke of Kent, who had opened the additional Medical School Buildings on that same day.

De Crespigny Park is named after the De Crespignys, Protestant refugees who came from France in the reign of William III and Mary; they eventually settled in Camberwell in the early part of the eighteenth century. A later descendant was Sir Claude Champion de Crespigny—whence the names Champion Hill and Champion Park.

Near an Elizabethan mansion, the 'Old House on Camberwell Green', long since demolished, was a residence built for George, Prince of Denmark—hence the name Denmark Hill.

At the beginning of 1800 there lived at the Grove, Camberwell, the celebrated Dr. John Coakley Lettsom, F.R.S. (1744–1815), a wealthy Quaker physician. At his country house—Grove Hill—with five acres of garden, he entertained some of the eminent literary men of his time. Boswell, Dr. Samuel Johnson's biographer, was a frequent visitor there. In 1770 Lettsom founded the General Dispensary in Aldersgate Street, the first of its kind in London, and he established the Royal Sea-bathing Infirmary at Margate in 1796. He founded the Medical Society of London in 1773, and the early meetings of the Society were held in his house in Sambrook Court, Basinghall Street, City.

Lettsom was a fervent disciple of his friend Edward Jenner (1749–1823) and an active supporter of the then recently introduced vaccination for the prevention of small-pox.

Dr. Lettsom used to sign his prescriptions 'I. Lettsom', hence the following epigram:

> When any sick to me apply,
>   I physicks, bleeds and sweats 'em:
> If after that they choose to die,
>   What's that to me,
>   I. Lettsom.

Ruskin Park, named after Ruskin, is an open space of thirty-six acres on Denmark Hill. It was acquired in 1907 and 1910 by the

London County Council and the Borough Councils of Lambeth, Camberwell, and Southwark.

John Ruskin (1819–1900) was the son of John James Ruskin, who died in 1864 and left his only son John a large fortune, an imposing house, now known as Ruskin Manor, and extensive grounds on Denmark Hill. John Ruskin continued to live there with his mother until she died in 1871, when he left Denmark Hill and went to live at Brantwood, an old cottage and property on Coniston Water, where he died in 1900.

Bessemer Grange, formerly the home of Sir Henry Bessemer, and Bessemer Road are named after the inventor of the steel-making process.

At the bottom of Dog Kennel Hill stood the Huntsmen's Lodge; it was demolished in the widening of the road. The Medical School Sports Ground on Dog Kennel Hill was once the headquarters of the Brixton Wanderers' Cricket Club.

THE HAMBLEDENS

King's College Hospital on Denmark Hill is a lasting monument to the initiative, the magnanimity, and the munificence of the Hon. William Frederick Danvers Smith, later Viscount Hambleden (the second). William Frederick D. Smith was the only surviving son of the Right Hon. W. H. Smith, M.P., who was leader of the House of Commons under Lord Salisbury in 1886 (see *King's*, p. 358).

William Henry Smith, Jnr. (1825–1891), whose father largely developed the firm of Messrs. W. H. Smith & Son, was a Donor of the First Class to, and became a firm supporter of, King's College, London, after it was founded in 1829. Later he became a Life Governor of the College, a member of the Committee of Management of the Hospital in 1849, and was elected a Vice-President of King's College Hospital in 1875 (see *King's*, pp. 180–1).

The Hon. W. F. D. Smith joined the Council of King's College, London, in 1894 and remained a member of it until his death. He accepted the onerous office of Treasurer of King's College in 1896, and was Chairman of the Delegacy of the College from its inauguration in 1910.

He was elected Chairman of the Building Committee of the 'Removal Fund' of the Hospital in 1904 and became Chairman of the Committee of Management in succession to General Lord Methuen, G.C.B., in 1908.

In 1904 he purchased the site of about twelve acres on Denmark Hill and presented it to the Committee of Management of the

Hospital. The Hon. W. F. D. Smith was a generous contributor to the cost of erecting the present Hospital and the Medical School; and he contributed over £200,000 to the funds of the Hospital.

Lord Hambleden (the second) may be regarded as the Founder of the third King's College Hospital.

In 1920 he became the Patron of King's College Hospital Medical School Clubs and Societies Union, and two years later he formally opened the War Memorial Pavilion on the Medical School Athletic Ground at Dog Kennel Hill; the free use of the ground he allowed to the Clubs and Societies Union (see *King's*, p. 380).

William Frederick Danvers Smith, second Viscount Hambleden, died on June 16, 1928. He had been a Vice-President of the Hospital since 1894 and Chairman of the Committee of Management since 1908. He was succeeded by his eldest son the Hon. William Henry Smith, who became governing director of Messrs. W. H. Smith & Son, Strand House, Portugal Street, W.C.

Viscount Hambleden (the third) was born on July 25, 1903, and educated at Eton and New College, Oxford; he became a member of the Committee of Management of the Hospital in 1928, and, after the death of Earl Beatty, he was elected Chairman in 1936; in 1937 he became appointed a Vice-President of the Hospital.

Viscount Hambleden (the third) continued to carry out his duties as Chairman with generosity and devotion to the interest of King's until illness overtook him in 1947; during his absence the duties of Chairman were carried out by the Vice-Chairman, Mr. (later Sir) William Gilliatt. Viscount Hambleden resigned the Chairmanship of the Committee of Management on February 1, 1948, but retained his membership of the Committee. He was succeeded in the office of Chairman by the Marquess of Normanby. Viscount Hambleden died somewhat suddenly after an operation on March 31, 1948. He is greatly missed at King's, where his interest in the Hospital and all that concerned it was ever manifest.

The Dowager Viscountess Hambleden became a member of the Committee of Management of the Hospital in 1920. She resigned in 1935, but rejoined the Committee during the period of the War (1939–45). Her kind advice and support have been of the greatest value to the Committee; her tact and enthusiasm never failed. Her daughter, the Hon. Edith Smith, was elected a member of the Committee of Management in 1935 and her daughter-in-law, the Viscountess Hambleden, was elected in 1936; both of whom became active members of the Committee.

The Viscountess Hambleden is President and Chairman of the

VISCOUNT HAMBLEDEN (THE THIRD)
Chairman of King's College Hospital, 1936–48

Hospital Linen Guild, and the Hon. Edith Smith is the Honorary Secretary.

Lord Herbert, son of the fifteenth Earl of Pembroke and brother-in-law of Viscount Hambleden (the third), was a member of the Committee of Management from 1934 to 1944.

KING'S COLLEGE HOSPITAL, DENMARK HILL

At the main entrance to the Hospital there are two commemoration stones; the one on the left as the Hospital is entered is engraved as follows:

> This stone
> was laid by
> His Majesty,
> King Edward
> The Seventh.
> July 20th, 1909.
> (See Pl. 5).

and the one on the right is as follows:

> This Hospital
> was opened by
> His Majesty,
> King George
> the Fifth,
> July 26th, 1913.

THE ADMINISTRATION BLOCK

The William Henry Smith Block

The Administration Block is centrally placed with the Casualty and Out-patient Department to the east, the Medical School to the west, and the Chapel at the centre. The Administration Block contains the Secretarial Offices, the Board Room, Registrars' Rooms, Dining Rooms, the Resident Medical Officers' Quarters, and the Nurses' Quarters.

William Henry Smith, father of William Frederick Danvers Smith (second Viscount Hambleden), became a Governor of King's College Hospital in 1841 and a member of the Committee of Management in 1849. He joined the Council of King's College in 1867 and was elected a Life Governor of the College in 1879.

In the main entrance hall of the Hospital there are two memorial tablets; one is to the memory of William Henry Smith and the other to the memory of William Frederick Danvers Smith.

1825   In Remembrance   1925
June 24th.
William Henry Smith
Memorial Building

In Memory of the Right Honourable
WILLIAM HENRY SMITH, M.P.
Formerly First Lord of the Treasury,
A Member of the Committee of Management
of King's College Hospital from 1849
to 1874, and a Vice-President from 1874
until his death in 1891.

In Memory of
WILLIAM FREDERICK DANVERS SMITH,
afterwards Viscount Hambleden.
Vice-President of the Hospital 1894
Chairman of the Committee of Management
1908–28, and its most generous benefactor.
His selfless devotion will be held in
Remembrance as an inspiration to all
who work here.

[See *King's*, p. 382.]

THE BOARD ROOM OF THE HOSPITAL

Upon the walls of the Board Room are the portraits of some distinguished members of the Hospital. Their names are as follows:

Lord Lister, O.M., F.R.C.S., F.R.S.
Surgeon and Consulting Surgeon from 1877 to 1912
(over the mantelpiece)

Dr. William S. Playfair, M.D., LL.D., F.R.C.P.
Assistant Obstetric Physician, Obstetric Physician, and Consulting Obstetric Physician, 1863–1903.

Sir William O. Priestley, M.D., LL.D., F.R.C.P.
Obstetric Physician and Consulting Physician, 1863–1900.

Mr. T. G. Sambrooke
Member of the Committee of Management (1839–71).
Vice-Chairman, 1846, 1850, and 1854.

Sir George Johnson, M.D., F.R.C.P., F.R.S.
Assistant Physician, Physician, and Consulting Physician, 1847–96.

KING EDWARD VII LAYING THE FOUNDATION STONE OF KING'S COLLEGE HOSPITAL,
DENMARK HILL, ON JULY 20, 1909

This picture is reproduced with the kind permission of the Daily Mirror

Sir William Fergusson, Bt., F.R.C.S., F.R.S.
Surgeon, 1840–77.

Sir Alfred Baring Garrod, M.D., F.R.C.P., F.R.S.
Physician and Consulting Physician, 1862–1907.

Mr. Robert Cheere
Member of the Committee of Management (1839–76).
Vice-President, 1858.
Treasurer of the Hospital, 1870–6.

Sir Frederic Still, K.C.V.O., M.D., LL.D., F.R.C.P.
Assistant Physician, Physician, and Consulting Physician for Diseases of Children, 1899–1941.

The Hon. W. F. D. Smith (second Viscount Hambleden)
Chairman of the Committee of Management, 1908–28.

Admiral the Right Hon. Earl Beatty, P.C., G.C.B., O.M., G.C.V.O.
Chairman of the Committee of Management, 1933–6.

There is also a sculptured head in marble of

Sir Alfred Baring Garrod, M.D., F.R.C.P., F.R.S.
Physician to King's College Hospital, 1862–74.

THE HOSPITAL

The main corridor of the Hospital is 900 feet in length from east to west; opening out of it are the six (one unnamed) ward blocks with the contained wards extending southwards towards Ruskin Park, and the Stock Exchange Wing for private patients. At the west end of the main corridor is the double special ward block (Hambleden Block), containing four wards, each ward accommodating fifteen beds.

The wards generally are so arranged that they catch the maximum amount of sun. Each ward is heated by radiant heat and low-pressure steam-radiators. There are twenty-four beds in each of the general wards and at the end of each ward there is a sun balcony overlooking Ruskin Park for the use of patients. The operating theatres are set on the north side of the main corridors.

At the east end of the Hospital, adjacent to Denmark Hill, are the Casualty and the Out-patient receiving rooms, waiting hall (capable of seating 500 persons), and the consulting rooms.

An 'observation ward' contains beds in separate glass-screened cubicles.

THE WARD BLOCKS

The King Edward VII Block was named by the permission of King George V.

The King George V Block was also named by the permission of King George V.

The Hasker Block is named in accordance with the conditions of a gift of £20,000 to the Removal Fund of the Hospital, from the executors and trustees of the late Miss Marianne Frances Hasker.

The Edward Yates Block is named at the request of his son, Mr. F. C. Yates, in consideration of a gift of £20,000 to the Hospital Removal Fund.

The Hambleden Block is named in recognition of the services rendered to the Hospital by the late W. F. D. Smith (second Viscount Hambleden).

THE WARDS

The Wards on the First Floor

Matthew Whiting Ward. In April 1902, at the request of Mrs. Matthew Whiting, a ward was named after the late Mr. Matthew Whiting in recognition of his bequest to the Hospital.

Twining Ward. Named in 1852 after Richard Twining II, F.R.S. (see p. 6).

Lister Ward. Named in 1913 after Lord Lister, Surgeon to King's from 1877 to 1893 (see p. 3).

Storks Memorial Ward. Named by reason of a bequest in 1903 of £20,000 by Robert Reeve Storks in memory of his father Mr. Serjeant Storks.

Lonsdale Ward. Named in memory of the Rev. Dr. John Lonsdale who was prominent in the establishment of the Hospital. He was a member of the Provisional Committee of King's College in 1828 and a member of the original Council appointed in 1829. He remained a member of the Council until he died in 1867. He was Principal of King's College from 1839 to 1843, Archdeacon of Middlesex 1842, and Bishop of Lichfield from 1843 to 1867 (see *King's*, p. 18).

Fisk Ward. Named after the Rev. J. H. Fisk, who had given £1,600 to the funds of the Hospital. He was Vice-President in 1839 (see *King's*, pp. 37 and 41).

Cheere Ward. Named after Mr. Robert Cheere, appointed a member of the Committee of Management in 1839, Vice-President, 1858, Treasurer, 1870–76 (see *King's*, p. 104).

The Wards on the Second Floor

Sambrooke Ward. Named after Mr. T. G. Sambrooke, a member of the Committee of Management (1839–71) and Vice-Chairman in 1846, 1850, and 1854.

Annie Zunz Ward. Named in compliance with the conditions governing the donation of £10,000 made by the trustees of the 'Annie Zunz Bequest' to the Building and Equipment Fund of the Hospital, dated November 7, 1912.

Victoria and Albert. Named after Queen Victoria and her Consort Prince Albert.

Fergusson Ward. Named after Sir William Fergusson, Surgeon to the Hospital from 1840 to 1877.

Todd Ward. Named after Dr. Robert Bentley Todd, a founder of the Hospital, Physician to King's from 1840 to 1859 and the first appointed Dean in 1842.

Waddington Ward. Named after Miss Anne Waddington in 1897 (see *King's,* p. 207).

George Trundle Ward. Named after Mr. George Trundle in 1918 by reason of a gift of Stocks of the nominal value of £10,000.

The Wards on the Third Floor

Pantia Ralli Ward. The Children's Medical Ward, named in 1866 by reason of a gift of £6,500 presented by Mr. Peter Pantia Ralli in order to perpetuate the memory of his father Mr. Pantia Ralli.

Princess Elizabeth Ward (previously the Wigram Ward; see *King's,* p. 365). The Children's Surgical Ward, named in 1929 by permission of Her Royal Highness the Duchess of York, later Her Most Gracious Majesty the Queen.

THE STOCK EXCHANGE WING

This wing was opened on February 23, 1937, at the invitation of Mr. R. B. Pearson, Chairman of the Stock Exchange, by Colonel the Right Hon. the Viscount Wakefield of Hythe, G.C.V.O., C.B.E., LL.D., Vice-President of the Hospital (see p. 74).

The tower over the entrance to the Stock Exchange Wing is named the Giles Guthrie Tower.

In front of the Stock Exchange Wing is the statue of Dr. Robert Bentley Todd (see *King's,* p. 63), by Matthew Noble (1818–76).

THE CHAPEL

The Chapel is placed at the centre of the Hospital, and the Annual Service of Remembrance and Thanksgiving held in November is appropriate to an institution which is in origin a religious foundation.

The windows and internal fittings were transferred from the Chapel in the old Hospital and have been extended to meet the requirements of the larger building.

Morning and Evening Prayers are read daily in the Chapel either by the Sister Matron or her deputy.

On Sundays there is a service in the morning and another at 5.30 p.m. The latter is broadcast throughout the Hospital and can be followed by the patients as each bed is connected by a wireless apparatus installed in 1926 by the *Daily News* and each patient is supplied with headphones.

The Chapel is designed to seat 250 people. The pulpit, the lectern, the choir-stalls, and the seating were given by Charles Edwin Layton, a member of the Committee of Management of the Hospital, and by Rachel his wife, in 1900.

The Organ was built in 1889 by means of private subscriptions from members of the Committee of Management, the medical staff, sisters, nurses, students, and other friends of the Hospital.

The Reredos was erected by the subscriptions of grateful nurses and friends to the memory of Katharine Henrietta Monk, Sister Matron of King's from 1885 to 1906 (see p. 34).

The Windows in the Chapel are to the Memory of:

Clara Sibbald Anderson Peddie, Home Sister, 1888–95.
Edward Montague Forster, Secretary, 1874–7.
John Hernaman, A.K.C.
Rev. Nathaniel Bromley, A.K.C., Chaplain, 1878–1901, and Warden, 1889–1901.

Other Memorials in the Chapel are to the Memory of:

Lionel Smith Beale, M.B., F.R.C.P., F.R.S., Physician and Consulting Physician, 1856–1906.
Captain H. S. Tunnard, Secretary, 1901–17.
Jocelyn Johnstone (*née* Almond), House Surgeon and House Physician, 1922.
Charles Blake Lewis, a former student of King's.
James T. Lilburne, B.A., M.R.C.S.
Eveline Jane Edmonds, Almoner, 1910–38.
Elise Margaret Kemp, Sister, 1908–17.
Anne Cole, Nurse in the Surgical Wards for over ten years.
Lily Ernst, Probationer Nurse, died 1914.
Nora J. Sewell, Nurse, 1920–3.
Wilma Bridges Stewart, Nurse, 1914–17.

In the side chapel there is a window to the memory of Mary Elizabeth Ray (Sister Elsie), Sister Matron from 1906 to 1918 (see p. 41).

On the Wall of the Vestibule are the following Memorial Tablets:

David, Earl Beatty, Chairman, 1933–6.
Ernest Laurence Levett, K.C., Vice-Chairman, 1915–16.
Robert Frederick Norton, C.B.E., K.C., Vice-Chairman, 1916–28.
George Loraine Hawker, Vice-Chairman, 1934–7.
Wilfrid Stanley Hatch, M.A., Resident-Chaplain, 1934–7.
George Heyer, M.B.E., M.A., Appeal Secretary, 1923–5.
Harold Waterlow Wiltshire, O.B.E., D.S.O., and Ellen Wiltshire, his wife.
Charles Nathaniel Read, Acting House Physician, died 1918.
Katharine Corstorphine Todd, R.R.C., Sister (see p. 49).
Fanny Irene Sprake Jones, Q.A.I.M.N.S.R.
Lydia Langton Hunter, Sister, 1912–16.
Mabel Patricia Scovell, Sister, 1905–7.
Vera Doreen Hunnyball, Nurse, 1925–8.
Mary Dorothy Lucine Wall, Nurse, 1922–5.
Margaret, Wife of Sir Watson Cheyne, Bt., F.R.S.
Frederick James Knapp, Head Master of St. Matthew's Boys' School, Denmark Hill.

War Memorial Tablets

1914–1918

King's Men

G. L. Atkinson	E. W. Carrington	A. L. Goff	A. H. Lister
D. Aucutt	S. Clark	S. G. Hare	A. B. McBride
J. F. Baddeley	W. B. Clark	S. H. Hodges	S. C. Philson
E. A. Bell	R. S. Cocke	J. James	P. B. Ridge
T. G. Brodie	H. J. Deller	H. A. de Lautour	J. S. Ricketts
A. W. B. Carless	G. B. Flux	P. Levick	J. R. Waddy

Kunwar Indarjit Singh

Works Staff

Thomas Norman Stewart
Charles Smith

Porters

Herbert Albert Howes
William Cowell

Nursing Sisters

Florence D'Oyly Compton
Fanny Irene Sprake Jones
Elise Margaret Kemp
Elizabeth Robinson
Wilma Bridges Stewart

MEMORIAL TABLETS IN THE MEDICAL SCHOOL

In the Library

John Raymond Waddy, M.C.
House Surgeon 1913–1914.
Lieut. R.A.M.C.
Killed in the Bois de Ploegsteert,
March 17th, 1915.

Donald Aucutt,
Captain, Royal Warwickshire Regiment.
Killed at Rentel, Flanders, October 9th, 1917.

In a Class Room

Edward Worrell Carrington, M.C.,
House Surgeon, 1914.
Captain, R.A.M.C.
Killed in France, September 27th, 1915.

In the Pathological Laboratory

Percy Brewster Ridge.
Assistant Pathologist.
Captain, R.A.M.C.
Died on March 12th, 1916.

SECTION III

THE NURSING DEPARTMENT OF KING'S

THE first Matron to be appointed when the Hospital was acquired in January 1840 was Mrs. Ward. She and some of her domestic staff took up their abode in the Hospital on April 2. It was stipulated at the time of her election that the Matron should be between 30 and 50 years of age, and that her salary should be at the rate of £50 per annum.

Mrs. Ward engaged three nurses and three helpers for the opening of the Hospital on April 15, 1840, which then contained fifty beds. The domestic staff consisted of the cook, Matron's maid, housemaid, and scullery maid. By the end of that year seventy more beds were added and the nursing staff was accordingly increased, three more nurses and four more helpers being engaged.

The women who nursed the patients in the early days of the Hospital were for the most part uneducated and many of them were ignorant of the duties which they were required to perform.

In the preface of *Martin Chuzzlewit*, which Charles Dickens commenced in 1843, he tells that the nurses who appear in it—Betsy Prig and Sarah Gamp—were portraits drawn from life. The latter was never separated far from the whisky bottle, and no doubt many of the so-called nurses at that period were dram-drinkers and even liked their pipe of tobacco.

Nursing in the early days at the Hospital was far from satisfactory, and during the period from 1848 to 1856 the state of things appears to have become worse. It seems that many women of inadequate experience, coarse manners, questionable character, and even of bibulous tendencies were employed in the wards, much to the distress of the patients, the annoyance of the medical staff, and the demoralization of the students.

In consequence of this unsatisfactory state of affairs, Miss Florence Nightingale (Lady Superintendent of a Home for Invalid Gentlewomen in Chandos Street, London, founded in 1850 by Viscountess Canning) was in August 1854 requested to take the post of Superintendent of Nurses and to institute a training school for nurses in connexion with King's. It is believed that Miss Louisa Twining (see p. 7) was anxious that Miss Nightingale should be asked to come to King's and that she actually did come to the Hospital in order to ascertain the condition of the nursing and of the nursing staff.

Before she was able to arrange anything definite in connexion with the nursing at the Hospital, the Crimean War had broken out and she was requested to go to the Crimea to superintend the nursing of the wounded and sick soldiers.

Florence Nightingale (1820–1910) was born in Florence on May 12, 1820. From an early period in her life she had manifested much sympathy with affliction in any form, and an urge to devote herself to the solace of suffering was always with her. She commenced her vocation by visiting hospitals within reasonable distance of her home at Lea Hurst, Derbyshire. She eventually went to many country towns and to London visiting reformatories, workhouses, and hospitals, observing particularly the general administration of the institutions and the various methods of nursing.

She soon came to the conclusion that a staff of educated nurses was absolutely essential for nursing, and that a school for training nurses in their duties was required. She learned that such an establishment already existed on the Continent. Accordingly in 1851 she entered the Institution of Protestant Deaconesses at Kaiserswerth on the Rhine as a voluntary nurse and remained there for six months. Later she studied with the Sisters of St. Vincent de Paul the system of nursing and hospital management in Paris.

The idea of the establishment of an institution for training nurses had occurred to others as well as to Miss Nightingale, for in 1848, largely through the influence of Bentley Todd, William Bowman, Arthur Farre, and Lionel Beale (all King's men), with the co-operation of the Bishop of London, the St. John's House and Sisterhood, Queen's Square, Westminster, an institution for training women of education as nurses on a religious basis, was founded.

The nurses trained there were taught to regard their work as a holy function, and to devote their lives to the care of the sick and destitute.

During the period of 1848–56 the St. John's House Sisterhood and King's College Hospital were in no way connected, except that the four King's men already named had an interest in both institutions.

MISS FLORENCE NIGHTINGALE AND THE CRIMEAN WAR

In October 1854 Miss Nightingale accepted the invitation of the Hon. Sidney Herbert,[1] Secretary of State for War, to organize a staff of nurses, and with them to go to the Crimea.

---

[1] Sidney Herbert, the first Baron Herbert of Lea (1810–61), was the second son of George Augustus, the eleventh Earl of Pembroke. He was Secretary of State for War under Sir Robert Peel from 1845 to 1846, and under the Earl of Aberdeen from 1852 to 1855 (during the Crimean War).

Accompanied by thirty-four nurses from St. John's House, Miss Nightingale left England on October 21 and went to Constantinople. They arrived at Scutari in Asiatic Turkey on November 4, just in time to receive the wounded soldiers from the Battle of Balaclava, fought on October 25.

Miss Nightingale set to work with masterly vigour and carried out her well-arranged plans. Under her admirable management the general confusion of the hospital at Scutari soon became orderly, and the sanitary arrangements improved. Within a few months after her arrival she had 10,000 sick and wounded soldiers under her care, and, in spite of severe fever, she stuck to her post until Turkey was evacuated by the British in July 1856.

'The experiment which this gifted lady made on a colossal scale in the Crimean War had had the effect of completely changing the entire hospital system of our Country and indeed of Europe' (Dr. James Taylor, in a *History of the Nineteenth Century*).

Edward Atkinson[1] (see *King's*, p. 68) while House Surgeon at King's College Hospital in 1855, was selected with J. Whitaker Hulke (see *King's*, p. 123) and some others to go out to the Crimea to aid the Army Medical Service which had broken down. They worked with Florence Nightingale at Scutari. After the War in 1856 Atkinson was appointed Surgeon to the British Hospital at Jerusalem and upon his return to England in 1860 he became appointed Surgeon to the Leeds Infirmary.

Miss Nightingale returned to London on September 8, 1856, somewhat broken in health but honoured by her country. From Queen Victoria she received an autograph letter of thanks and a cross set with diamonds. A fund of £50,000 was raised as a testimonial to her, but she requested that it might be applied to founding an institution for training nurses, and so the *Nightingale Fund*, of which Sir William Bowman was a member until he died in 1892, was instituted (see *King's*, p. 110).

The Nightingale Training School and Home for Nurses was founded as a memorial to her at St. Thomas's Hospital in 1860, and in that school she took a deep personal interest. There is no doubt that it was Florence Nightingale who first aroused the public mind to the need that existed for trained nurses. She commenced the reform of nursing in this country and raised nursing to an honoured vocation. As a published Government pamphlet puts it, 'the nursing profession, as it exists to-day in this country, owes its origin to the work of Florence Nightingale'.

[1] Edward Atkinson died on March 1, 1906.

In 1860 she published a valuable book *Notes on Nursing*, and later she assisted in founding the Red Cross Society.

At the conclusion of the Crimean War, at the suggestion of Dr. Bentley Todd, the Committee of Management of King's appointed a sub-committee, consisting of Mr. Thomas G. Sambrooke, Mr. W. H. Smith, Mr. F. Wiggett, Mr. (later Sir) William Fergusson, and Dr. Bentley Todd, to inquire into the efficiency of the Hospital nurses.

The outcome of the report of the sub-committee was that Mr. C. P. Shepherd, the Master of St. John's House, was approached, and eventually the Committee of Management of the Hospital opened negotiations with the committee of that institution, and on March 31, 1856, an agreement was reached by which the nursing at King's was to be undertaken by the sisters of St. John's House.

On one morning early in May 1856, the previous nursing staff of the Hospital, booted, shawled, and bonneted, stood lined up in the front hall of the old Hospital ready to march out immediately after the sisters and nurses of St. John's House had walked in.

The expressions of the old nurses and their undertoned remarks may be readily imagined!

After this change there was almost immediately a great improvement in the nursing and in the general conduct in the Hospital. At the end of the year the Rev. Dr. Jelf, Principal of King's College, commented on 'the inestimable influence of the presence of these ladies upon the character of the medical students'.

Dr. Bentley Todd said: 'There are no persons connected with our Hospital, who would come forward more warmly, more cordially, and I may say, more vociferously, and would cheer the ladies more heartily than our medical students, and that, I think, is strong practical testimony to the great and important value of the fusion of these two establishments.'

After her return from the Crimea Miss Nightingale visited King's and expressed herself highly gratified at the new arrangements which had been effected in the nursing department and remarked especially on the cleanly, cheerful, and home-like appearance of the wards.

In 1860 Mr. Robert Williams of Birchin Lane presented to the Hospital £1,000 which had been placed at his disposal for charitable purposes by Mr. Samuel Francis Wood of Hickleton, Yorkshire. This donation enabled the Committee of Management to add an additional story to the Hospital and place it at the disposal of the sisters and nurses of St. John's House, many of whom had previously been compelled to put up with limited accommodation in the older part of the building.

For a few years all appears to have gone reasonably smoothly in the nursing department, but early in 1873 trouble arose between the Committee of Management of the Hospital and the Committee of St. John's House. The dispute seems to have arisen about the Sister-in-Charge at the Hospital and related especially to some minor matters of administration. Towards the end of 1873 the Committee of Management of the Hospital asked that the Sister-in-Charge should be relieved of her post and another sent in her place. The Committee of St. John's House, after consideration, absolutely refused to comply with this request and appealed to the Council of King's College which was thus drawn into the dispute.

On December 17, 1873, the Council of King's College came to the conclusion that 'the agreement between the two bodies does not entitle the Committee of Management of the Hospital to require from St. John's House the withdrawal of the Sister-in-Charge'!

In reply the Committee of Management of the Hospital on February 1, 1874, gave due notice that in six months it would terminate the existing agreement with St. John's House and would then organize its own system of nursing.

Then began an unfortunate controversy between the Committee of Management of the Hospital and the Council of King's College, and, worse still, the matter was taken up in the public press.

The Council of the College then intervened between the Committee of Management of the Hospital and the Committee of St. John's House, and eventually the points at issue were referred to the arbitration of Lord Hatherley and Lord Selborne, both of whom were the legal members of the Council of the College. A compromise was finally attained whereby certain difficulties about cooking, washing, and the like were removed, but the offending Sister-in-Charge, concerning whose procedure the trouble had arisen, remained at her post. Consequently many members of the Committee of Management of the Hospital resigned, including Major-General Daubeney, the Vice-Chairman, and Mr. J. S. Waldron, the Secretary. Lieut.-General Sir Richard Wilbraham, K.C.B., a member of the Council of the College, became the new Vice-Chairman, and Mr. Edward M. Forster was appointed Secretary.

As a direct result of this unpleasant difference between King's College and the Hospital authorities, the funds of the Hospital were adversely affected. Moreover, as time went on it became increasingly evident that Sir William Fergusson and the Committee of Management were right when they contended that it was essential for the smooth working of the Hospital that the resident medical officers, the nursing staff, and the servants of the Institution should be under one and the same authority, i.e. the Committee of Management.

The nursing at the Hospital continued to be carried out by the sisters of St. John's House until 1885. During 1884 and the earlier part of 1885 the nursing arrangements were again carefully considered and discussed by the Committee of Management of the Hospital of which Lord Francis Hervey was Chairman. It was finally decided by the Hospital authorities to end the agreement with the Sisterhood of St. John's House which had existed since 1856, and to establish their own nursing staff and training school for nurses. The Committee decided to offer the post of Sister Matron to Miss Katharine Henrietta Monk, who was a member of the Sisterhood of St. John. The salary attached to the post was £100 per annum with an allowance for uniforms. Miss Monk accepted the post and came on duty in August 1885.

There is no doubt that the Rev. Dr. Henry Wace, Principal of King's College, who became Chairman of the Committee of Management in 1886, had a great deal to do with the reorganization of the nursing arrangements which took place soon after Sister Katharine was appointed Sister Matron (see *King's*, p. 174).

KATHARINE HENRIETTA MONK
'Sister Katharine'
Born, January 2, 1855.   Died, February 20, 1915

Miss Monk was Sister Matron and Superintendent of the Training School for Nurses at King's from August 5, 1885, until May 26, 1906, when she retired through ill health.

She was officially connected with the Hospital from 1883 and was acting Sister Matron from May 1884.

Katharine Monk in 1874 commenced nursing at the Hospital for Incurables, Edinburgh, when she attended nursing lectures and classes at the Royal Infirmary. In 1878 she became a probationer nurse at St. Bartholomew's Hospital, and obtained her Certificate of Proficiency in 1879, the year in which these certificates were first issued to nurses in the British Isles. For some years, as a certificated hospital-trained nurse, she was engaged in private nursing for Mr. (later Sir) Thomas Smith of St. Bartholomew's Hospital, and was particularly chosen to nurse babies after their operation for hare-lip.

In 1883 she was appointed Night Sister at King's and at Charing Cross Hospital, being on duty at one or the other as directed by the Sisterhood of St. John's, for both these hospitals were at that period nursed by the St. John's House Sisterhood. The night-nursing staff

KATHARINE HENRIETTA MONK
First Sister Matron of King's College Hospital
Photograph kindly lent by Miss E. A. Jackson

of the Sisterhood was housed in Norfolk Street, Strand. Later in 1883 Miss Monk became a Ward Sister at Charing Cross Hospital.

In May 1884 she was requested by the Superior of the St. John's House Sisterhood to return to King's as Sister Matron and to act under the direction of the Sister Superior of St. John's House who was Chief-in-Charge.

In July 1885 Miss Monk resigned her appointment in consequence of trouble between the St. John's Nurses and the Hospital authorities, and applied at the War Office for nursing work. She was appointed Superintendent of a company of nurses about to go to the Sudan to serve during the Egyptian campaign. At the last moment and at the personal request of Lord Francis Hervey, Chairman of the Committee of Management of King's, she withdrew from the War Office appointment and agreed to become Sister Matron at King's upon the retirement of the Sisterhood of St. John's House. She actually commenced her duties at King's on August 5, 1885.

Miss Monk, with wonderful tact and efficiency, gradually reorganized the Nursing Department, founded the Training School for Nurses, and later established a private nursing staff at King's. She arranged courses of lectures and demonstrations by members of the medical staff for the nurses and also instituted tutorial classes.

In her arduous work she was ably assisted by Sister Phillipa Hicks, who was appointed Home Sister in 1887.

One of Sister Katharine's first acts was to discharge all the nurses who had worked under the St. John's Sisterhood and to introduce an entirely new set of nurses. The quick change which she effected took place smoothly and without the slightest upset in the wards. It is said that, when all was ready, her new staff walked in at one door as the nurses of St. John's House walked out at the other.

By this wise step she quickly re-established trust and confidence between the members of the medical and nursing staffs.

Sister Katharine was an ideal Sister Matron. She was a kind but strict disciplinarian of the highest moral principles, but most sympathetic and helpful to any sister or nurse in difficulty. She attempted to instil into each nurse that nursing the sick was not a profession but a *vocation*; moreover she taught her nurses that they were to act as loyal and helpful handmaids, neither more nor less, to the members of the Medical Staff of the Hospital.

She soon became extremely popular with the members of the honorary medical staff, with the students, and with the nurses.

The writer, who was House Surgeon in 1894, testifies personally to her many kind and sympathetic deeds.

Miss Monk appointed Ward Sisters in whom she had the greatest confidence, and she never interfered with their ward management.

After a few months Miss Monk lost her loyal assistant, Home Sister Phillipa Hicks, who left King's on her appointment as Matron at the Hospital for Sick Children, Great Ormond Street.

Miss Monk was fortunate in obtaining on April 25, 1888, as the new Home Sister, Miss Clara Sibbald Peddie, daughter of Dr. Alexander Peddie of Edinburgh. Miss Peddie received her nursing training in the Nightingale School of St. Thomas's Hospital (see p. 31). Sister Sibbald soon became a most loyal and helpful colleague to Sister Katharine. She had a wide knowledge of medical and surgical nursing and was able to teach massage to those nurses whom she had specially selected.

In 1892 Sister Katharine and Sister Sibbald gave an interesting lecture-demonstration on nursing and massage before a large gathering of King's College Hospital Medical Society (see *King's*, p. 449).

Sister Sibbald was a wise Superintendent of the Nurses' Home. She, too, was a strict disciplinarian, but nurses felt that they could always go to her for helpful advice. She died suddenly at King's following an operation in 1895.

Miss Monk was a short, active figure usually dressed in black alpaca with white cap and apron. She moved briskly, and seldom a day passed in which she did not visit each ward. Nothing appeared to escape her notice with regard to cleanliness in general, and the comfort of the patients in particular. She was not only highly respected by the whole of her staff, but was much loved by many.

She was a pioneer for longer off-duty times for her nurses. Probationers were on duty from 7 a.m. until 9 p.m. with four hours off-duty daily, together with half an hour allowed for dinner and tea. In each day-room there was a list of off-duty times and each nurse when going on duty in a fresh ward was allotted a distinctive number, 1, 2, 3, or 4, so she could ascertain at a glance when she would be off-duty and could then make her engagements accordingly. Numbers 1, 2, and 3 had duties allotted which covered all the probationers' ward work. Number 4 was relief nurse for the other numbers and took 'off-duty' times. Late leave was not easily obtained, as Sister Katharine believed that a nurse could not be out late and up early the following morning without injury to her health.

A staff nurse's (third-year probationer) 'off-duty' time daily was either from 10 a.m. to 2 p.m. or 6 to 10 p.m. and once a week was 7 to 11 a.m. She was then allowed either to have a late breakfast at 9.25 a.m. or go out of the Hospital to breakfast. Day-nurses were allowed one day off-duty a month, whereas night-nurses were allowed two nights off-duty a month. Sisters and staff nurses were allowed a week-end off-duty once a month. These off-duty times were not altered unless there was a shortage of nursing staff or illness amongst the nurses.

The system of training proved to be most satisfactory, and except for slight modifications and the establishment in 1924 of a Preliminary Training School, where the nurses spend the first eight weeks of their training, the Sister Matrons following Miss Monk have had little reason to change it. It has been copied by other hospitals at home and abroad, especially in those cases where 'King's' nurses have been appointed as Matron.

In the nineties the Operation Theatre was staffed from the Fergusson Ward, then a small female surgical ward, but each sister took charge of her own operation cases except when an emergency case was brought from a medical ward, when the sister of Fergusson Ward took charge.

In the theatre there was a nurse-in-charge and an assistant nurse. The sister on duty at night took charge of the night operation cases.

In the old King's College Hospital the nurses were required to make their own beds, sweep and dust their bedrooms, the floor of which was polished once a week by a maid.

The outdoor uniform of the nurses, consisting of a grey alpaca frock, long black cloth cloak, and black bonnet with a black veil hanging to the waist at the back, had to be worn when 'off-duty'. The sisters had much the same outdoor uniform except that they wore green dresses and the black veil at the back reached to the level of the knee. Sister Matron wore a black dress and her veil was worn a little longer than those of the sisters.

The outdoor uniform was certainly a protection to the sisters and nurses in the days of the old Hospital (see p. 1). Sisters and nurses were required to obtain permission to wear 'mufti' on the days when they were 'off-duty'.

King's nurses were allowed to use the Inns of Court Library Garden in Lincoln's Inn, which afforded them periods of quiet for reading and study.

There is no doubt that in the old Hospital under Miss Monk's superintendence the nurses were a happy and contented crowd both when 'on' and 'off-duty'. There was that happy feeling amongst them of belonging to one big family, which, in the larger hospital of to-day, is not to the same extent possible.

Any of her staff who revisited the Hospital would probably find

Miss Monk seated at her office desk. She would rise quickly and welcome the caller with the motherly greeting, 'Well, my child, I am glad to see you'.

Sister Katharine would never pass a nurse, student, or 'resident' on the staircase or along the corridor without giving a cheery word or a bright smile. The secret of her daily life was trying to put into action the words 'Whatsoever He saith unto you, do it', which were graven on the little silver cross which she wore, and in carrying out part of her daily prayer, 'Teach me, dear Lord, Thy holy will; help me my duty to fulfil'.

There was a short service in the Hospital Chapel for the nursing staff and maids morning and evening at which Miss Monk usually officiated. She frequently deputed the Home Sister to read prayers while she acted as organist. Her favourite hymns were: 'God, that madest earth and heaven' (*A. & M.* 26) and 'The day Thou gavest, Lord, is ended' (*A. & M.* 477).

On Sundays there were services at 8 a.m. and 6 p.m., and at the latter, at which the Hospital Chaplain officiated, sisters, nurses, patients, and sometimes resident medical officers were present.

A small booklet compiled by Miss Monk was handed by her and by each succeeding Sister Matron to every nurse on her admission to the Training School at the end of her trial period. In it these words are to be found:

Laborare est Orare
(Work is Prayer)
That noblest work is noblest praise,
Though life is full of care,
Each deed of love shall sing above,
And make our life a prayer.

'Inasmuch as ye have done it unto one of the least of these my brethren, ye have done it unto Me.'

'Let all nurses remember that discipline and obedience are the key note to satisfactory and efficient work in life; for to rule well we must first learn how to obey. Let them bear in mind that they must ever be loyal, generous, tender and gentle; yet strong in action and thought, avoiding any remark that would tend to take from the delicacy and refinement of their work; not forgetting that the life depends upon the acceptance of a training that will further its objects and help to enable the workers to regard that work and life as a great privilege granted to them to be efficiently and humanely performed.'

KATHARINE HENRIETTA MONK.
    Sister Matron and Superintendent of
    the Nurse Training School of King's
    College Hospital, 1885–1906.

CHRISTMAS-TIDE IN OLD KING'S

When Miss Monk was Sister Matron, by five o'clock in the morning of Christmas Eve, Sister Katharine, the Home Sister, the Ward Sisters, and day-nurses were at Covent Garden Market amidst the flowers and bustle, surrounded by the flare and glare of the market lights, threading their way between the various stalls to choose the best flowers and plants which they could afford. When the purchases were over one of the ubiquitous Irish women, frequenting the market with an eye to business, would be chosen to carry the booty in a basket poised on her head back to the old Hospital. After the usual coin had been proffered, on which she would 'spit for luck', she would shower fervent blessings on the members of the party and the good 'Old Orspital'.

Decoration of the Chapel and dining-halls with flowers, and the wards and staircase with flowers and other devices went on apace, sisters, nurses, residents, and students all taking their share.

On Christmas Eve the residents' piano was usually drawn into the main hall and placed beneath the shadow of the statue of Dr. Bentley Todd, dressed to impersonate Father Christmas. The Sister Matron—Miss Katharine Monk—at the piano, surrounded by the resident medical officers, the accident dressers for the day, the Ward Sisters, those of the nursing staff not on duty, ward-maids, and all of the domestic staff who could manage to be present, joined in the singing.

Just before the clock struck 11.30 the Night Sister quickly traversed the corridors and set the ward doors open so that the patients might hear the strains of the Christmas carols which were sung by the assembled company. At 12.0 midnight the Old Hospital Chorus was sung by the whole company standing (see *King's*, p. 228).

In the early nineties the finances of the Hospital were at an alarmingly low ebb, whereupon Miss Monk not only enforced the strictest economy amongst the nursing staff but approached the Duke of Westminster, who kindly allowed a Meeting of Appeal to be held at Grosvenor House over which he presided. The result of the meeting was so successful that the Committee of Management was enabled to carry on.

Miss Monk was a member of several committees outside King's. She joined the Committee of the Royal Pension Fund for Nurses at its inauguration in 1887. By command of Queen Alexandra, Miss Monk was one of the first two Civil Matrons appointed on Queen

Alexandra's Imperial Military Nursing Service Advisory Board for the improvement and reorganization of Military Hospitals, and later she was appointed by the command of King Edward VII and Queen Alexandra one of the Council of the Red Cross Society.

Miss Monk became a member of the Building Committee of the new Hospital in 1904, and took an active part in planning its Administrative Department. Her main idea was that the new Hospital should be constructed upon the general principle of 'centralization with radiation', and with 'continuity yet separation'. Mr. Pite, the architect, took a keen interest in Miss Monk's plans and with some modification carried out her well-considered scheme.

In October 1905 Miss Monk suffered from a severe illness. As soon after convalescence as possible she returned to the Hospital, but only to find she was unable to bear the full strain of her office. She therefore resigned her Sister Matronship and left King's on May 26, 1906.

Her standard of nursing was exceedingly high and her life was one of loyal service and self-sacrifice.

She was present at the ceremony when King George V and Queen Mary opened the new 'King's' at Denmark Hill on July 20, 1913.

Katharine Henrietta Monk died on February 20, 1915, at the Free Eye Hospital, Southampton, where her sister, Miss A. M. Monk, was Matron. After a service in St. Paul's Church in that town, her body was buried in the Southampton cemetery.

By an unfortunate mistake her Christian name of Katharine was inscribed 'Catherine' on the headstone of her grave.

MEMORIAL TO KATHARINE HENRIETTA MONK

A Memorial to Miss Katharine Monk was arranged by a committee of which Viscount Hambleden was Chairman. For twenty-one years she had been Sister Matron at King's and during that time she founded the Nursing School of the Hospital and inspired its special characteristics.

THE REREDOS IN THE HOSPITAL CHAPEL

On November 1, 1917, a Service of Dedication of the Reredos, the Memorial to Katharine Henrietta Monk, the first Sister Matron of the Hospital, was conducted in the Hospital Chapel by the Lord Bishop of Southwark, Chaplain to the Hospital, who was assisted by the Very Rev. Dr. Henry Wace, Dean of Canterbury.

Dr. Wace wrote the inscription on the Monk Memorial:

'To the Sacred Memory of Katharine Henrietta Monk,
Sister Matron of this Hospital, 1885–1906.
'Blessed are they that do His Commandment that they may have the right
to the Tree of Life and may enter through the Gate into the City.'

At the base of the reredos is written:

'Inasmuch as ye have done it unto one of the least of these my brethren,
ye have done it unto Me.'

An inscription by the Sister Matron's pew in the Hospital Chapel
is as follows:

'To the sacred memory of Katharine Henrietta Monk,
Sister Matron of this Hospital, 1885–1906.
'She founded its Nursing Home on those principles of Christian Devotion,
Charity and Loyalty which inspired her own life.
'Whatsoever He saith unto you, do it.
'The Reredos of this Chapel was erected by the subscription of grateful
nurses and friends.'

THE MONK MEMORIAL PRIZE

The Monk Memorial Prize Fund was raised as a memorial to
Katharine H. Monk.

The annual income of the Fund is awarded twice a year together
with a certificate which indicates that 'The Monk Memorial Prize
is for General Proficiency, Excellent Conduct, Loyalty and Devotion
to Professional Duties' and is awarded to the nurse who obtains the
first place in the bi-annual final examinations of the nursing staff.

The first nurse to obtain the prize and the certificate was Miss
E. M. Tirard (now Mrs. Trumper), daughter of the late Sir Nestor
Tirard (see *King's*, p. 413), and the second nurse to whom the prize
was awarded was Miss K. F. Armstrong, who afterwards for twelve
years was Sister Tutor (see p. 47).

MISS MARY ELIZABETH RAY (1864–1933), R.R.C.

Sister Matron, 1906–18

Miss Elsie Ray joined King's as a special probationer in 1889 when
she came under the direct influence of Miss Katharine Monk. Her
first post as sister (Sister Elsie) in 1892 was in the Albert Ward.
In 1893 she became sister in the Pantia Ralli and King's College
Wards, where she was an excellent teacher of nursing. In 1896 she
was appointed Assistant Matron at the Leeds General Infirmary, and

after serving that institution for three years she became Matron at the Lincoln General Hospital in 1899. On the retirement of Miss Monk from King's in 1906, Sister Elsie returned to King's as Sister Matron, a post which she held with distinction until 1918 when she retired.

Miss Ray was appointed a member of the Building Committee of the present Hospital and many of the improvements in the arrangements in the building are due to her interest and practical advice. To her fell the task of assisting in the transference of the Hospital from Portugal Street to Denmark Hill and the rearranging of the nurses' training so as to meet the requirements of the new Hospital.

When the European War broke out in August 1914 and the larger portion of King's became the 4th London General Hospital (Territorial Army), Sister Elsie donned the red-trimmed grey military uniform of an army sister and became the Principal Matron of the combined military portion of the Hospital and its extensions in Ruskin Park, and the civil part of King's, also of the Maudsley Hospital and the neighbouring schools, a task which she performed with infinite tact and wise judgement. For her services she was awarded the Royal Red Cross.

From 1909 to 1918 Miss Ray had the able assistance of Sister Isabel (Miss Isabel Brown), who at first was Home Sister, but in 1913 was appointed Assistant Matron.

After Miss Ray retired from King's in 1918 she continued to work as Honorary Secretary of Lady Minto's Indian Nursing Association, but she retained her interest in King's, acting as Secretary of the Hospital Linen Guild and as Patron of King's College Hospital Nurses' League from its foundation in 1924.

Her kindness and thoughtfulness for others were beyond words; she was indeed a loyal friend and a wise counsellor, and she loved King's.

Miss Ray died in the Lister Side Ward of the Hospital on December 31, 1933, after three days' illness.

MEMORIALS TO MARY ELIZABETH RAY

In the Side Chapel of the Hospital is a stained-glass window placed there by Miss Ray's sisters. It was dedicated on All Souls' Day, November 2, 1934, by the Rev. R. V. Galer, who was for many years Resident Chaplain at King's.

A Memorial Fund was established in 1934 and the sum of just over £500 was collected by a committee appointed for the purpose.

In the name of trustees the money was invested and the annual interest is distributed at the discretion of the Sister Matron in conjunction with the Home Sister to members of the Hospital nursing staff needing assistance, especially those who require rest during convalescence after illness.

A tablet, designed by Mr. W. A. Pite, architect of the Hospital, was fixed at the instance of Professor Albert Carless on the wall by the swing doors leading from Sister Matron's corridor to the Hospital Chapel:

'This Tablet has been placed here in loving memory of Mary Elsie Ray who devoted the greater part of her life to the service of King's College Hospital. Nurse 1889; Sister 1892–1896; Sister Matron 1906–1918. She died in the Hospital on New Year's Eve, 1933. Her many friends have subscribed to the M. E. Ray Memorial Fund for the Assistance of King's Nurses. There can be no Memorial more fitting of one whose life was an example of practical religion and whose thoughts were always for others.'

This memorial was unveiled at the Annual Memorial Service held in the Hospital Chapel and taken by the Bishop of Gloucester, the Right Rev. Dr. A. C. Headlam on All Saints' Day, November 1, 1935.

The Bishop said: 'For fineness of character, serenity of temperament and dedication to her calling, they could have no saintlier example than Miss Ray.'

MISS M. A. WILLCOX, O.B.E., R.R.C.
Sister Matron, 1918–37

Miss Willcox commenced her training at King's College Hospital, Lincoln's Inn Fields, in 1905 under Katharine Monk and continued it under Elsie Ray. She was the last probationer passed into the Training School by Miss Monk. After the usual three years in the nursing department at King's, Miss Willcox went to the Royal Free Hospital as Ward Sister for eighteen months, and in 1910 to Manchester as Matron of a surgical nursing-home.

In 1914 she was called up for service as sister of the Territorial Force Nursing Service and arrived at King's on August 14. She was sent to 'Todd Ward', which had not been furnished, and was instructed to equip it as quickly as possible. With the help of four staff nurses of the Territorial Force Nursing Service and two orderlies, one of whom was a bank manager and the other a member of the Stock Exchange, the ward was soon ready to receive fifty patients. The first to arrive were wounded soldiers from France, and later Belgian soldiers injured during the retreat from Mons, the stationmaster of Mons being among them.

In May 1915 Miss Willcox was sent to Alexandria as Charge Sister at 15th General Hospital, and in five months she was appointed Matron of the Officers' Hospital in Cairo. From Egypt she returned to King's in 1916 as Assistant Matron of the Army Huts in Ruskin Park, an extension of the 4th London General Hospital (King's College Hospital) which was joined to King's by a temporary bridge over what is now the Southern Region of British Railways.

In April 1918 Miss Willcox was appointed Sister Matron of King's in succession to Miss Ray. Hers was a formidable task, for she had to re-establish the civilian Hospital as it became slowly evacuated by the military. She also helped to organize the use of some wards for private patients.

During Miss Willcox's tenure of office at King's she brought about many changes one of which was to provide smoking-rooms for her staff. She, with Mrs. M. Purkis and Miss A. Gray-Buchanan, founded the King's College Hospital Nurses' League in 1924 (see p. 52).

Miss Willcox arranged for the appointment of a Sister Tutor in 1919. In 1924 she was instrumental in establishing a Preliminary Training School for nurses, in which an opportunity is given for girls who have already received their general education to obtain a course of instruction in elementary nursing and domestic arts.

During the period that Miss Willcox was Sister Matron there was a large increase of the nursing staff. Her first report to the Nursing Committee of the Hospital dealt with 11 sisters, 41 staff nurses, and 44 probationers—96 in all; her last report dealt with 31 sisters, 105 staff nurses, and 119 probationers—255 in all. Under her aegis some 821 nurses have been trained at King's, and since Todd Ward became part of the Midwifery Training School in 1920, 102 nurses have obtained the C.M.B.

Miss Willcox was a natural leader, a far-seeing and capable organizer, ever ready to consider suggestions for the improvement of the conditions under which the nurses in her charge had to work. She did much to diminish the amount of domestic work which is usually required of nurses, so that more time could be devoted to the nursing and care of the patients.

In 1935 Miss Willcox was awarded the King George V Jubilee Medal in recognition of her work for fifteen years as a member of the Advisory Board of the Princess Mary's Royal Air Force Nursing Service. She was also a member of Queen Alexandra's Army Nursing Board and Queen Alexandra's Imperial Military Nursing Service for six years.

Upon Miss Willcox's retirement in 1937 the Committee of Management placed on record their profound gratitude for the long and devoted service that she had rendered to King's during her tenure of office. Before their meeting on July 29, 1937, the Chairman presented to her a silver inkstand, suitably inscribed, and a cheque from the members of the Committee and the Medical Board.

Miss Willcox was elected a member of King's College Hospital Ladies' Association, also a member of the Council of the Cowdray Club and of the Voluntary Advisory Nursing Board of the Prison Commission.

During the war (1939–45) Miss Willcox became Deputy to Dame Johanna Cruickshanks, D.B.E., R.R.C., Matron-in-Chief of the British Red Cross Society, and she worked in the Trained Nurses' Section of the British Red Cross Society and St. John Ambulance Association.

MISS M. K. BLYDE, O.B.E., R.R.C.
Sister Matron, 1937–47

Miss M. K. Blyde, who succeeded Miss Willcox as Sister Matron, began her nursing experience as a V.A.D. from 1914 to 1919, and in 1919 she joined the Training School at King's. After the completion of her course of training she was appointed sister (Sister Mercia) of Fisk and Cheere Wards and had charge of the Aural Theatre. She left King's to take up the duties of Assistant Matron at the Norfolk and Norwich Hospital; thence she became Matron of the West Suffolk General Hospital, Bury St. Edmunds, a position she occupied for a little over nine years.

After returning to King's Miss Blyde was appointed a member of the Nursing Advisory Committee of the British Red Cross Society.

When war was declared in 1939 King's was established as Sector IX of the London Emergency Medical Service and Miss Blyde became the Sector Matron. The Sector Headquarters were at Sherwood House, Epsom, and as Miss Blyde had of necessity to spend much of her time at the Sector Headquarters, Sister Elizabeth (Miss G. L. Buffard) was appointed Acting Sister Matron at King's during Miss Blyde's absence.

Miss Dorothy Dixon (Civil Nursing Association) went to Sector IX and became Assistant Matron at the War Emergency Hospital, Leatherhead, and Mrs. Miller (Nurse G. Rigden) went to the Horton

War Emergency Hospital, Epsom, as an Administration Sister, both of these former King's nurses acting under the direction of the Sector Matron, Miss Blyde.

In 1946 Miss Blyde was appointed an officer of the Order of the British Empire.

Miss Blyde retired from King's on March 31, 1947, and was succeeded by Miss E. A. Opie, D.N. (London University), the first Assistant Matron at Guy's.

Following her retirement Miss Blyde was chosen to represent the Hospital and King's College Hospital Nurses' League at the Congress of the International Council of Nurses, which was held in Atlantic City, U.S.A., in May 1947. Later in the year she became Vice-President of the National Council of Nurses of Great Britain and Northern Ireland.

MISS ISABEL BROWN
Assistant Matron, 1913–21

Miss Isabel Brown trained at Pendlebury Children's Hospital, Manchester, from 1888 to 1891 and at King's from 1891 to 1894. She remained at King's until 1895, when she went to the Hospital for Sick Children, Great Ormond Street, as Ward Sister, and subsequently as Night Sister from 1896 to 1899. She was Ward Sister at St. George's Hospital from 1899 to 1907.

Miss Brown returned to King's in 1909 as Home Sister and Lecturer to the Nurses and became the first appointed Assistant Matron when the Hospital moved to Denmark Hill in 1913. She continued as Lecturer to the Nurses until the appointment of Miss A. M. Bishop as Sister Tutor in 1919.

In the office of Home Sister Miss Isabel Brown was succeeded in 1914 by Miss Mary M. Wylie.

MISS ELEANOR COOKE, R.R.C.
Assistant Matron, 1921–35

Miss Eleanor Cooke finished her training at King's in 1914 and during the War (1914–18) she was a member of the Territorial Army Nursing Service. In 1919 she returned to King's and was appointed Night Sister (Sister Eleanor), subsequently becoming Home Sister. On the retirement of Sister Isabel (Miss Isabel Brown) in 1921, Sister Eleanor was appointed Assistant Matron.

During her fourteen years' service at King's Miss Cooke was the right hand of Sister Matron, Miss Willcox. Her influence was of the highest possible value in maintaining those high standards of conduct and efficiency which for many years past have been characteristic of King's nursing staff.

Her work was greatly appreciated by the members of the honorary and nursing staff.

In 1935 Miss Cooke retired and was succeeded in the office of Assistant Matron by Miss G. L. Buffard.

After leaving King's Sister Eleanor received a gift from the members of King's College Hospital Nurses' League, and in her letter of thanks she wrote: 'For all of us there is no place like King's and it has been my great privilege to work with Sister Matron for sixteen years, and try however humbly to uphold our great traditions.'

In the early days of the War of 1939 Sister Eleanor (Civil Nursing Reserve) offered her services to King's; they were gratefully accepted and she once more returned to the Sister Matron's Office.

MISS KATHERINE FRANCES ARMSTRONG, D.N.
Sister Tutor, 1923–37

Before coming to King's for her training as a nurse, Miss K. F. Armstrong had a distinguished career at the University of Reading, of which she was a scholar, and later for a time she taught in public schools for girls.

She entered the Training School at King's in 1916 and at the end of her course in 1919 she was awarded the Monk Memorial Prize. She obtained the C.M.B. and was appointed Assistant Night Sister and subsequently Ward Sister at King's. Later she obtained the Sister Tutor's Diploma of the Battersea Polytechnic, and the Diploma of Nursing granted by the University of London, and was for a time Sister Tutor at the Royal Northern Hospital.

In 1923 she returned to King's as Sister Tutor in succession to Miss A. M. Bishop, who had held the post since 1919.

Sister Frances was a brilliant teacher and had the gift of being able to inspire enthusiasm in her pupils. She will long be remembered with gratitude by King's nurses and by nurses of other nationalities who came to King's as international students of the Florence Nightingale Foundation (see p. 31); and also by the students of the Medical School to whom she gave many useful lecture-demonstrations.

In 1937 Miss Armstrong resigned her post as Sister Tutor on accepting the editorship of the *Nursing Times*, the official journal of the Royal College of Nursing. She was succeeded in the tutorship by Miss M. I. Otway.

For fifteen years Miss Armstrong edited the King's College Hospital Nurses' League *Journal*. In this office she was succeeded by Miss M. Houghton.

MISS M. IRENE OTWAY
Sister Tutor, 1937

In 1937 Miss Otway succeeded Miss K. F. Armstrong as Sister Tutor. Miss Irene Otway received her nursing training at King's; she became appointed Assistant Night Sister and later Assistant Sister Tutor.

After leaving King's she held the posts of Ward Sister and Sister-in-Charge of the Out-patient and Casualty Departments at the West Suffolk General Hospital. Before returning to King's she was Sister Tutor and Home Sister at the Royal United Hospital, Bath.

MISS EMMA DURHAM, R.R.C. AND ZULU WAR MEDAL

At the time of her death in 1936 Emma Durham was one of the oldest members of King's College Hospital Nurses' League. She died in Sambrooke Ward on October 31, aged 89; she left some interesting reminiscences of her early training at King's.

Emma Durham joined St. John's Nursing Sisterhood and entered St. John's House, Norfolk Street, Strand, in September 1872 and continued her training at King's until 1875.

During that period the probationers were aroused at 6.30 a.m. and after their seven o'clock breakfast, each with a little basket of personal provisions of butter, tea, and sugar for the day, they walked in crocodile fashion under the eyes of the sister from St. John's House to King's College Hospital, Lincoln's Inn Fields, to be on duty in the wards by 7.45 a.m. There were at that period twenty-four beds in each ward and to each ward there was attached a sister, a nurse, an assistant nurse, and a probationer. With the exception of two hours (2 to 4) off-duty in the afternoons of every *other* day, the probationers were on duty until 8.30 p.m., when they returned two and two to St. John's House. The night duty for the probationers was 9.45 p.m. to 7.45 a.m., and hard work at that!

After leaving King's in 1875 Miss Durham with another King's nurse, Miss Allen, joined the Universities Mission to Central Africa and went to Zanzibar to inaugurate the first hospital there. Miss

Durham's first patient was David Wainwright, the African who took David Livingstone's heart and buried it under a tree. She also nursed the three Africans who carried his body across Africa to the coast.[1] Miss Durham did nursing not only in central Africa but also in Egypt, France, Germany, Italy, Belgium, Switzerland, Russia, and in America. She joined the King's College Hospital Nurses' League at its foundation in 1924 and never missed a Reunion.

MISS KATHARINE CORSTORPHINE TODD, R. R. C.

Miss K. C. Todd (Sister Katharine) received her training in K.C.H. in Portugal Street and obtained her nurse's certificate in 1904.

She remained at King's for twelve years, during the greater part of that period as sister of Todd and Cheere Wards.

At the outbreak of the War in 1914 she became a member of the Territorial Nursing Service at the 4th London General Hospital (K.C.H.), and in January 1915 she joined the British Expeditionary Force in France. She became Matron of four different clearing stations and took part in the retreat from the Somme in March, 1918. She was twice mentioned in dispatches and was awarded the R.R.C.

In 1919 Miss Todd opened a nursing home in Mentone and she became an active member of the Mentone branch of the British Legion until her death on December 28, 1937.

A tablet to her memory was placed in the vestibule of the Hospital Chapel on June 25, 1938.

MISS MARJORIE GREENER (SISTER PATRICIA)
Night Sister, 1920–39

Miss M. Greener received her training at King's from 1907 to 1910 and on its completion she returned to her home in South Africa.

She became Matron of a nursing home in Johannesburg, and in 1917 she worked as a member of the Imperial Nursing Service at a base hospital in Capetown.

She returned to England as Matron of a repatriation ship leaving Africa in October, reaching England in December 1919. Before leaving South Africa she wrote to Miss Willcox (Sister Matron), who arranged for her to come to King's for temporary duty—staff nurse in Lister Ward—on January 1, 1920.

---

[1] Dr. David Livingstone died of dysentery at Ilala, central Africa, on May 1, 1873. His body was embalmed, carried to the shore, put on board a British cruiser, and on April 18, 1874, it was interred in Westminster Abbey.

In August 1920 she succeeded Miss Eleanor Cooke as Night Sister and retired from that post in November 1939.

Nineteen years as Night Sister is a wonderful record, and the Hospital and Nursing School have indeed been fortunate in having the devoted and loyal service of Sister Patricia ('Sister Pat') for so long. She will be remembered with sincere gratitude by innumerable patients and their friends, by her colleagues and many night-staff nurses and probationers with affection, and by the resident medical officers with much appreciation for her kind help in cases of emergency and difficulty.

Sister Patricia was succeeded as Night Sister by Miss J. Wainwright.

THE NURSES' ANNUAL DANCE

In 1938, and for the first time, the Nurses' Annual Dance, under the superintendence of the Sister Matron, Miss M. K. Blyde, and with the permission of the Dean, John B. Hunter, was held in the Medical School and was a great success. In January 1939 the Nurses' Dance was again held in the Medical School and was a most successful evening.

To the nurses of to-day, with their reading, writing, smoking, shampoo, and ironing rooms, with their dances, Lawn Tennis Club, and Swimming Club, with the 'Randall Challenge Cup,' together with the Nurses' Amateur Dramatic Society inaugurated in 1929— the conditions as in the Hospital at Portugal Street must appear to have been somewhat primitive. But it was in those earlier days under the influence of Miss Monk that tradition was being made, and it is the individuals who make the name of a hospital and help to build its traditions. It is essential that these King's traditions be upheld and handed on from one generation of nurses to another.

In spite of many changes which have occurred with the passing of time and the moving of the Hospital from Portugal Street to Denmark Hill, 'King's' with its unique atmosphere is still much the same.

SOME PREVIOUS WARD SISTERS

During the year 1939 three former Ward Sisters of King's passed over:

Miss Agnes Mary Owen (Sister Agnes), previously trained at the Middlesex and St. Bartholemew's, came to King's in 1885 and served King's for eight and twenty years, during the greater portion of which she was Sister-in-Charge of Fisk Ward in the old Hospital. She died on January 4, 1939.

Miss Emily Kate Synge, A.R.R.C. (Sister Kate), was trained at the Liverpool Hospital for Children and at King's. She came to King's in 1890 and was Ward Sister during part of the last three years (1890–3) that Sir Joseph Lister was Senior Surgeon. After leaving King's she was appointed Matron of the Royal Chest Hospital, City Road, and later she was head of the Church Army Home for Children at Fleet. Miss Synge died at Hindhead on July 25, 1939.

Miss Mary Frances Lightfoot, R.R.C. (Sister Frances), was trained at the Liverpool Hospital for Children and at King's, which she entered in 1893. She was Theatre Nurse at the end of Sir Joseph Lister's time at King's and later Ward Sister for over twenty years. During the South African War (1899–1901) she became one of Queen Alexandra's Nurses and was in charge of the operating theatre at Nauwport Hospital and at Johannesburg. During the War of 1914–18 she was Matron of the Officers' Hospital, Fishmongers' Hall. She possessed great organizing ability and upheld the highest traditions of nursing. Miss Lightfoot died on July 2, 1939.

MRS. EMMA SOTON

Emma Soton, who had been connected with King's for more than thirty years, passed to her rest on October 10, 1940. She had been maid to the nurses' dining-room, parlour maid to the residents' dining-room, personal maid to Miss M. E. Ray, and latterly in charge of the Nurses' Bureau, where she had a cheery greeting for all comers. She retired from King's in 1931.

Sister Matrons at King's

Miss Katharine H. Monk, 1885–1906.
Miss Mary Elizabeth Ray, r.r.c., 1906–18.
Miss M. A. Willcox, o.b.e., r.r.c., 1918–37.
Miss M. K. Blyde, o.b.e., r.r.c., 1937–47.
Miss E. A. Opie, 1947.

Assistant Matrons

Miss Isabella Jane Armisted, 1896–8.
Miss Isabel Brown, 1913–21.
Miss Eleanor S. Cooke, r.r.c., 1921–35.
Miss Grace L. Buffard, 1935–44.
Miss Margaret A. Stagg, 1944.

Second Assistant Matrons

Miss Joyce L. Ryde, 1941–47.
Miss Eileen M. Giles, 1947.

Home Sisters

Miss Kate *Phillipa* Hicks, 1887–8.
Miss Clara *Sibbald* Peddie, 1888–95.
Miss (*Isabel*) Isabella Jane Armisted, 1895–96.
Miss *Marcia* C. Barker, 1896–1901.
Miss *Alice* H. Little, 1901–9.
Miss *Isabel* Brown, 1909–13.
Miss (*Margaret*) Mary Marsden Wylie, 1914–19.
Miss *Eleanor* S. Cooke, 1919–21.
Miss (*Elizabeth*) G. L. Buffard, 1921–35.
Miss G. *Monica* Matthews, 1935–41.
Miss C. *Eveline* Kirk, 1941–6.
Miss *Cicely* A. Brodie, 1946.

Sister Tutors

Miss A. M. Bishop, 1919–23.
Miss Katharine F. Armstrong, 1923–37.
Miss Mintrue I. Otway, 1937.

Night Sisters

Miss Marjorie Greener, 1920–39.
Miss Janet M. Wainwright, 1939.

KING'S COLLEGE HOSPITAL NURSES' LEAGUE

In 1916 five nurses, who had recently completed their training at King's and were about to leave the Hospital, decided that they would endeavour to meet again somehow and somewhere in five years' time and renew the friendships that they had formed at King's. They actually met within a year of the date which they had previously planned, but instead of the original five, some twenty King's nurses gathered together, and the success of the meeting, mainly due to the enthusiasm of Miss A. Gray-Buchanan, was such that they decided to meet again during the following year.

The next recorded meeting occurred in 1924, when about thirty nurses were present, and amongst their number were the Sister Matron, Miss M. A. Willcox, and a former Assistant Matron, Miss Isabel Brown. The Reunion was again a great success. Miss Willcox ascertained from those present that they were desirous that a League of King's Nurses should be formed and further that Miss Gray-Buchanan and Mrs. Purkis (Nurse M. Dabell) were willing to undertake the task of its inauguration.

Forthwith Miss Willcox called a meeting of King's nurses at the

Hospital on Saturday, June 21, 1924, at which it was decided to form a Nurses' League.

Accordingly office bearers were appointed, rules and regulations drawn up, and a badge of membership chosen.

The first officers of the King's College Hospital Nurses' League founded in 1924 were as follows:

PATRONS

Viscountess Hambleden
Miss M. E. Ray, R.R.C.

President	*Vice-Presidents*
Miss M. A. Willcox, R.R.C. (Sister Matron).	Mrs. Arthur Edmunds (Nurse M. Stratford). Miss Isabel Brown.
Joint Secretaries	*Joint Treasurers*
Miss A. Gray-Buchanan. Miss E. S. Cooke, R.R.C. (Assistant Matron).	Mrs. Purkis (Nurse M. Dabell). Miss G. L. Buffard (Home Sister).

Editor

Miss K. F. Armstrong
(Sister Tutor).

Committee

Miss M. E. Catherwood.
Mrs. Gibbins, R.R.C.
  (Nurse A. M. Raine).
Miss A. Hobill.
Miss Edith A. Jackson, R.R.C.
Miss Frances Lightfoot, R.R.C.
Miss Mary A. Peddie.
Mrs. Wright (Nurse S. Broadwood).

Miss W. M. Carpenter ⎫
Miss M. Greener ⎪
Miss G. M. Matthews ⎬ Residents.
Miss H. K. Noble ⎪
Miss D. Richardson ⎭
A staff nurse in training to attend all Committee Meetings.

The first Reunion of the League took place in the Hospital on June 6, 1925, over 200 members being present. Viscountess Hambleden presided and the meeting was addressed by Miss M. A. Willcox, Miss M. E. Ray, Miss K. F. Armstrong, and by Miss Emma Durham, who was the most senior member present (see p. 48). The oldest member to join the Nurses' League was Miss A. K. Barnes, who completed her training at King's in 1867.[1]

After tea a short service was held in the Hospital Chapel conducted by the Bishop of Woolwich, assisted by the Resident Chaplain, the Rev. C. S. Garbett, and two former Hospital Chaplains, the Rev. T. Parker and the Rev. R. V. Galer.

[1] Miss A. K. Barnes died in 1928.

The first King's College Hospital Nurses' League *Journal* edited by Miss K. F. Armstrong, was published in 1925. It contains the portraits of the last Lady Superintendent of the Nurses at King's who worked under the direction of the St. John's Sisterhood, of Miss K. H. Monk, Miss M. E. Ray, and Miss M. A. Willcox.

In 1925 the first 'League Stall' at the Hospital Fête was established in order to raise money to endow the 'League Bed' in the Hospital.

In 1926 the King's College Hospital Nurses' League Bed in Twining Ward was endowed. In the same year the 'Nurses League Benevolent Fund' was inaugurated. This fund is used for necessitous cases and any King's nurse is eligible for a grant. In 1934 the Benevolent Fund was augmented by a gift 'In Memory of Miss M. E. Ray' from her sisters. The Nurses' League received a legacy of a little over £3,600 from Miss M. E. Walder, who trained at King's from 1894 to 1897 and who died on March 7, 1935.

In 1931 the nursing staff collected amongst themselves and their friends £1,000 for the general fund of the Hospital.

In 1933 the Nurses' League sent a gift of £60 to the International Florence Nightingale Memorial Fund. The sum of £500, the larger portion of which was collected by Mrs. G. M. Miller (Nurse Rigden) from members of the Nurses' League, for the Nurses' Home Extension was handed to the Chairman of the Committee of Management at the Nurses' Hospital Fête on June 29, 1933.

In more recent years the Annual Reunion, usually held in the afternoon of the last Saturday in May or the first Saturday in June, consists of a luncheon in London followed by a General Meeting held in the Board Room of the Hospital at 3 p.m. After the meeting tea is provided in the Nurses' Dining-room, followed by a short service in the Hospital Chapel.

Gifts are usually received in the Board Room for the Nurses' Stall at the Annual Fête, as the sum of £60 each year is required to support the 'Nurses' League Bed' in Twining Ward.

The Coronation Nurses' Fête held at the Hospital in the summer of 1937 realized the sum of £1,000.

KING'S COLLEGE HOSPITAL
LINEN GUILD

THE *Needlework Guild* was originated in 1894 by Miss Katharine Monk, then Sister Matron, and by Miss C. E. Plunkett, sister of Miss P. K. Plunkett, who was Sister Kathleen from 1894 to 1898.

Working parties were arranged and the members commenced sewing energetically. At the end of each year's work there was a distribution of bed-jackets and other garments to the Ward Sisters. To these annual distributions the sisters usually went carrying sacks, prepared to take away as many articles as they could successfully annex.

The *King's College Hospital Linen Guild* became instituted and amalgamated with the Needlework Guild. The Guild then reconstituted consists of a Lady President, Vice-Presidents, life patrons, patrons, patronesses, and members, and is managed by a committee.

During the year 1913, when the Hospital in Portugal Street was vacated and the present Hospital opened, the officers of the Linen Guild were:

> *President:* Viscountess Hambleden.
> *Chairman of Committee:* Lady Watson Cheyne.
> *Honorary Treasurer:* Miss M. E. Ray.
> *Honorary Secretary:* Mrs. Arthur Edmunds.

OFFICERS FOR 1947–8

President and Chairman of Committee
Viscountess Hambleden

Vice-Presidents

Mrs. Benwell	Miss Holder
Miss M. K. Blyde, O.B.E., R.R.C.	Miss C. Perkin
Miss G. L. Buffard	Miss J. Ryde
Miss E. S. Cooke, R.R.C.	Miss Simpson
Mrs. Creed	The Hon. Edith Smith
Lady Gilliatt	Miss J. Stafford
Miss Gray-Buchanan	Miss A. Stagg
Mrs. Vernon Harcourt	Mrs. Aldren Turner
Miss E. M. Hodgkinson	Lady Wakeley

Miss M. A. Willcox, O.B.E., R.R.C.

Committee

Mrs. Castello	Mrs. Vernon Harcourt
Miss E. S. Cooke, R.R.C.	Mrs. Hunter
Lady Gilliatt	The Hon. Mrs. I. J. Pitman
The Dowager Viscountess	Mrs. Strong
Hambleden	Mrs. Aldren Turner
The Marchioness of Hamilton	Miss M. A. Willcox, O.B.E., R.R.C.

Honorary Secretary
The Hon. Edith Smith

Honorary Treasurer
Miss E. A. Opie, D.N.

Working parties are held in connexion with the Linen Guild and the amount collected for the Hospital by the Guild in 1947 was just over £162.

The Combined Annual General Meeting of the Linen Guild and the Ladies' Association is usually held in the Hospital some time in February or March.

KING'S COLLEGE HOSPITAL LADIES' ASSOCIATION

President
Lady Patricia Ramsay

The Honorary Secretary and Honorary Treasurer
The Hon. Mrs. Charles Tufton, O.B.E.

The Ladies' Association was originated by Viscountess Hambleden in 1917 with the object of furthering the cause of the Hospital in every possible way, particularly in raising funds; and it was reported in 1937 that since the foundation of the Association it had handed over to the funds of the Hospital over £85,000.

At the end of October 1942 Miss D. de M. Rudolf, who for many years had been the energetic Secretary of the Association, retired.

Although hospital conditions have become changed since the National Health Service has eventuated, the Ladies' Association has determined to carry on its work as hitherto.

There are six branches of the Association: the Central Branch; Herne Hill and Camberwell Branch; East Dulwich Branch; Dulwich and Sydenham Branch; North and North-West Camberwell and Peckham Branch; and Streatham and Brixton Branch.

During the War (1939–45) the East Dulwich Branch and the

Streatham and Brixton Branch appear to have been the most active in their efforts for King's. Some of the other branches lapsed during that period.

THE KINGFISHERS' SOCIETY

This Society is under the auspices of the Ladies' Association. In 1929 the 'Jolly Juveniles' or the 'Young Helpers of King's Society' was inaugurated, the prime mover being Miss N. L. Grey, who became its first Secretary.

At the first meeting of the Society some twenty-six members received their badges.

The 'Jolly Juveniles' undertook to raise £60 annually to support two cots: the 'Jolly Juveniles' cot in the Princess Elizabeth Ward and another later to commemorate the birth of Princess Margaret Rose.

In 1937 the Society changed its name to that of 'The Kingfishers', the members of which are fishers for King's. The officers then appointed were:

> Patron: The Hon. W. H. Smith.
> Chairman: Miss Everidge (later Mrs. Basil Francis).
> Vice-Chairman: Lady Helen Smith.
> Hon. Secretary: Mrs. E. M. Tuke.
> Hon. Treasurer: Mrs. Wansbrough.

There were then about sixty members of the Society.

The inaugural party of 'The Kingfishers' took place at the Hospital on May 1, 1937. There were 130 children present and subsequently many new members were enrolled. By the end of 1939 there were some 728 members of the Society, and in 1947 the numbers had increased to just over 1,000 members. The 'Kingfishers' hold a stall at the Nurses' Annual Fête and also organize special efforts to raise money on behalf of the Hospital. The Annual Party is usually held in the Medical School.

A 'Kingfishers' news leaflet under the editorship of Mrs. Bruce Pearson is published three times a year.

In 1947 the officers of the Society were:

> President: The Hon. Laura Smith.
> Chairman: Mrs. Neville Wade.
> Vice-Chairman: Viscountess Ruthven.
> Honorary Secretary: Mrs. Oakley.
> Honorary Treasurer: Miss D. de M. Rudolf.

In recent times the moving spirit of the Society is Sister Irene Otway, the Sister Tutor. During the war years she collected from the members just over £342 for the funds of the Hospital. Besides maintaining annually two cots in the Princess Elizabeth Ward the 'Kingfishers' have during 1947 given to the ward several articles of practical use.

CHEERFUL HELPERS' LEAGUE

The League, under the chairmanship of Mrs. E. Wiles and an energetic committee, holds monthly whist drives in the Garden Room of the Hospital, and thus adds to the finances of K.C.H. During 1943, £30 was handed over to the Hospital, in 1944 £50, and, since that date, yearly similar amounts have been given to the Hospital. On Hospital 'Flag Days' members of the League have rendered most efficient help.

In 1947 the League decided to carry on and to continue its efforts on behalf of K.C.H.

'THE WALRUS'

During 1931 a small journal *The Walrus*—'a friendly messenger to friends of King's College Hospital'—generously produced by an anonymous editor and entirely free of cost to the Hospital, became definitely established as the recognized medium through which information about the Hospital could be obtained; it was issued quarterly and had a circulation of over 7,000 copies.

THE IN-PATIENTS' LIBRARY

In the year 1857 a number of Theological Students of King's College, London, organized and managed a lending library for the use of in-patients in the first King's College Hospital. Unfortunately there is no record of the length of time that this service was continued.

In 1930, with the co-operation of Mrs. Gaskell, one of the trustees of the British Red Cross and of the Order of St. John Hospital Library, a free library for in-patients was established at King's.

A small Library Committee was appointed with Mr. A. D. Power as Chairman. For some considerable time Lady Mant acted as Librarian and she was ably assisted by many ladies. In 1931 a gift of books from the British Red Cross Society and the Order of St. John Hospital Library formed the nucleus of a central library by which the wards are served. By the year 1936 the In-patients' Library, at first instituted in a comparatively small way, had slowly developed so as to become a recognized hospital activity. A special Library Committee was then appointed with Mr. A. D. Power still acting as Chairman. Mrs. Hutton was the Head Librarian and she was fortunate in having many reliable lady assistants so that it became possible for each ward to be visited twice weekly.

In 1937 Mr. A. D. Power relinquished the chairmanship of the Library Committee; he was succeeded by Lord Herbert. In 1943 Mrs. Hutton, who had been Hospital Librarian for many years resigned; she was succeeded by Mrs. Holmes. For some time Miss Lees had been prominent in organizing and maintaining the library service.

SECTION V
THE ALMONER'S DEPARTMENT

MANY years have passed since, in the words of the Annual Report of the Hospital for 1904, 'the Committee are fully alive to the necessity of using every effort to ensure that the recipients of the charity are of the class for which it is intended, and as a further means of attaining this end, they have appointed an out-patient Lady Almoner from the 1st January, 1905'.

The first Lady Almoner to be appointed was Miss M. A. Lloyd Davies. In the Report of 1906 the Committee record 'their sense of the assistance received from the Lady Almoner', and also that 'the change in the character of the neighbourhood undoubtedly continues to be responsible in a great measure for the diminution in the number of out-patients, but the result is also partly due to the work of the Almoner's Department in assisting to eliminate patients who, by reason of their financial standing or from other causes, are unsuitable for hospital treatment'.

It may be of interest to examine the ways in which the work has progressed along the lines originally laid down and those in which it has altered. The work has developed and there have been modifications, but the spirit and the outlook have not changed, and the tradition has remained unaltered.

In 1905 in the old Hospital, the Lady Almoner had a small room in the basement, a corner partitioned off from the out-patients' waiting-hall. It was a depressing room, but perhaps because of the difficulties and of the need for strenuous effort, a good foundation was laid, and in the first twelve months—that is, up to the end of 1905— statements were taken of the circumstances of 8,307 patients. Of these, 1,387 were referred to clubs and dispensaries (under the heading of 'Thrift') and 143 were assisted with appliances and by other means. As over 8,000 patients were interviewed, it was obvious that one almoner could not investigate every case fully and also carry out the doctors' recommendations for those referred to her for special help, but her training did enable her to eliminate a considerable number of those who were abusing the free services offered by the Hospital and the medical staff. For six years the almoner worked alone, but in that short time the advantages of inquiry and adequate after-care were recognized by the Committee of Management, who then decided to appoint an assistant almoner.

The removal of the Hospital to Denmark Hill in 1913 increased the work for the almoners in the same unexpected degree as for all other members of the staff. It was soon apparent that even with most drastic limitation it was more than two trained women could accomplish. From that time the work has increased steadily, and the number of staff has been augmented, until, at the end of 1938, it consisted of six trained almoners, four clerks, one full-time voluntary worker, and four almoner-students.

In 1918 work had begun among in-patients, and in 1920 an almoner was appointed to deal specially with maternity patients.

Up to 1921 there was no almoner appointed to work among the patients attending the Venereal Disease Clinic, although any woman patient in obvious need of help was referred to the almoners and was assisted in a similar way to those attending other departments of the Hospital. When the London County Council co-operated with the Voluntary Hospitals in the organization of the Venereal Diseases Clinics, the opportunity for increased social work was met by the appointment of an almoner to work specially among those particular patients.

In 1925 a change was made in the administrative policy which affected the Almoner's Department almost more than any others. The Committee of Management then decided that all inquiries as to means should be made by members of the administrative staff, and that the duties of the almoners should be confined to 'social work' and 'after-care'. The general effect of this was that the number of patients interviewed by the almoners dropped to a small proportion of what it had been, but the assistance given was generally increased.

Previous to 1936 the almoner gave help and advice in the Diabetic Clinic when necessary, but in that year, through the generosity of the 'Sir Halley Stewart Trust', a part-time almoner was appointed to that department, and in 1937 a full-time appointment was made.

In the Asthma Clinic a full-time voluntary worker who had given her services since 1932, was regarded as a member of the almoner's staff.

It is interesting to compare the amount of money available as a Samaritan Fund for the almoner to allocate. In 1913 it was £20; later it averaged £500 per annum.

EVELINE JANE EDMONDS (1883–1938)
'Lady Almoner'

Miss Eveline J. Edmonds, the Head Almoner, died at Hove on July 11, 1938. She was educated at Putney High School and at

Somerville College, Oxford, obtaining an Honours Diploma in Mathematics in 1906; she also graduated B.A. of Trinity College, Dublin, in 1907. She was appointed mathematics and elementary science mistress at Putney High School, but her thoughts and inclinations turned to social work amongst the poor.

She was appointed Assistant Almoner at King's in 1910, becoming Senior Almoner two years later, and she was one of the last remaining links on the staff of King's connecting the present Hospital with the old Hospital in Portugal Street.

When Miss Edmonds was appointed, the Almoner's Department had been in existence only about five years, and the move to Denmark Hill resulted in a greatly increased scope as well as wider responsibilities. Miss Edmonds gathered around her a staff to whom her tireless energy and enthusiasm were an inspiration.

In more recent years the work of the almoners has gradually developed into an organized profession and Miss Edmonds undertook the training of students; many of those who took their practical course of instruction at King's will recall with grateful appreciation her infinite patience and her stern sense of duty.

The patients were her friends, and no trouble was too great for her to take on their behalf and no time too long for her to devote to them.

In Miss Edmonds King's lost a loyal and faithful servant. Miss Edmonds was succeeded at King's by Miss Jean J. Justice.

During the Service of Remembrance and Thanksgiving held on November 2, 1938, a memorial tablet to Eveline Jane Edmonds was unveiled by the Rev. Cyril Eastaugh, Chaplain to the Hospital, and a cheque was presented from her old colleagues and friends to perpetuate her memory as a Memorial Governor.

Lady Almoners at King's

Miss M. A. Lloyd Davies, 1905–12
Miss Eveline J. Edmonds, 1912–37
Miss Jean J. Justice, 1937–40
Miss M. Steel, 1940–4
Miss H. C. Simpson, 1944

THE PHYSICAL TREATMENT DEPARTMENT (PHYSIO-THERAPEUTICS)

IN 1911 Archibald D. Reid, who was in charge of the Radiological Department at King's, was appointed to the additional charge of the Massage and Physical Exercises Department. Electro-therapy came under the aegis of the Radiological Department at that time.

The newly formed Massage and Physical Exercises Department was then accommodated in one cubicle in the X-Ray Department, but later another room became available and was equipped as a Gymnasium for the treatment of cases of scoliosis.

At that period there were but four masseuses in the department, and they were almost entirely engaged in treating 'in-patients'. After patients were discharged from the wards, however, they received massage treatment as 'out-patients'.

In those days a masseuse usually had three months' training in massage only; no tuition in remedial exercises or in electro-therapy was given, although there were one or two training schools in which these subjects were taught.

The equipment at King's in 1911 consisted of one combined faradic and galvanic current table and a cell battery; when electrical treatment was prescribed, it was applied to the area to be treated by means of a roller electrode. Radiant heat baths had not come into common use, but there was a hot-air bath which was applied by a member of the nursing staff.

Archibald Reid was mainly interested in radiology, so that it was left to E. Bellis Clayton, the clinical assistant in the department, to organize additional work, particularly as he was anxious to develop the use of remedial exercises. At that period there were in London two private schools where students were taught Swedish remedial exercises, and from one of these, Mrs. Coghill Hawkes's School, the services of a qualified masseuse and three students were obtained in order to staff the new department.

In 1912 Archibald Reid (later Sir Archibald Reid) left King's to take an appointment in the Radiological Department at St. Thomas's Hospital (see *King's*, p. 318). He was succeeded in the Radiological Department at King's by Robert Knox, and E. B. Clayton was appointed Director of the Massage and Physical Exercises Department.

By the early part of 1913 the Out-patient Department and other portions of the Hospital at Denmark Hill, including that for physio-therapy, had been built and the accommodation in the new Hospital for physio-therapy consisted of a Hydro-therapy Department, a Finsen Light Room, an Exercise Room, and two rooms for immersion electrical baths.

When the new Hospital opened in October 1913, the Finsen Light Room was used for electro-therapy, a portion of the accommodation for hydro-therapy was used as the Massage Department, and the Exercise Room became the Gymnasium.

The newly organized department provided massage, Swedish remedial exercises, radiant heat, stimulation of muscles by means of faradic and galvanic currents, constant current treatment of various types, and sinusoidal current baths.

During the War (1914–18) a large portion of King's became the 4th London General Hospital and the work of the department became greatly increased. The Almeric Paget Massage Corps supplied King's with masseuses and much of the electrical treatment required for the soldiers was administered by members of the Corps in the department.

Sinusoidal current leg baths were used with success in the treatment of 'trench feet'. The work in the department became so heavy that voluntary workers had to be requisitioned to assist.

In 1915 the School of Physio-therapy was opened. The projected school had always been part of the scheme of the department so that assistants might be readily obtained. The outbreak of war in 1914 considerably delayed the formation of the school, but as masseuses were then needed more urgently than ever, it was decided to open the school in spite of the difficulties which existed.

Towards the close of the War in 1918 a special staff of masseuses, consisting mainly of former students of King's, was engaged to administer treatment to pensioners discharged from the Army. Day and evening sessions were arranged, and this special branch continued to function as long as it was required.

In 1919 the Orthopaedic Department of the Hospital was opened, with the result that work in the Physio-therapy Department was vastly increased, so much so that, in 1920, between 800 and 1,000 treatments per week were given. Later the doctors in the immediate neighbourhood of the Hospital sent their 'rheumatic patients' to King's for treatment; consequently the department became over-crowded. Temporary extra accommodation was provided in the Medical Casualty Department in the afternoons, but it was not until 1932 that the much-needed relief of the congested condition of the department was obtained by the provision of the hut which had been used as a refectory by the Medical School. The hut was removed to the piece of ground between the Massage and Almoner's Departments of the Hospital.

In 1925, through the good offices of the Stock Exchange Dramatic Society, an Ultra-violet Ray Department was instituted.

In 1935 the building in which the ultra-violet ray apparatus was housed had to be removed to make room for the new Private Patient Block which was then being erected. Other rooms were provided in the basement of the Hospital, and with this new accommodation a small Private Patient Physical Treatment Department was incorporated in which nurses and students as well as private patients received treatment.

The Physio-therapeutic Department, which was inaugurated in 1912, consists of a department for massage and remedial exercises, one for electro-therapy, one for ultra-violet ray treatment, and one devoted especially to the treatment of private patients and others connected with the Hospital.

Between 2,500 and 3,000 treatments are administered each week, and these are carried out by the students of the department under the supervision of a qualified and experienced staff. The patients for the most part are sent from the Out-patient Department of the Hospital, some come from medical practitioners in the surrounding districts, and many receive treatment in the Hospital wards.

During the last thirty years many changes have taken place in treatment by physio-therapy.

Massage now takes a less important place. Swedish remedial exercises have, to a considerable extent, been replaced by other exercises, and much more stress is laid on home exercises than hitherto. Radiant heat baths are still used, but in addition there are hot wax baths and the modern infra-red ray lamp. The technique of the treatments by the faradic and galvanic currents has been vastly improved. The old high-frequency current is used but little; it has largely been replaced by the diathermy current. Recently the ultra-short wave diathermy machine has proved to be valuable in the treatment of septic conditions. Another addition has been made in the Ultra-violet Ray Department, where arc lamps have been introduced for general and local irradiation.

Each addition to the various methods of treatment by physio-therapy has necessitated an increase in the time of training students; whereas in the early days of the department a course of three months was required, now the complete course of instruction extends over two years.

F

It is mainly due to Bellis Clayton's industry and unselfish efforts that the department over which he presided has risen to the high state of efficiency to which it has attained.

When Bellis Clayton retired from the office of Director of the Physio-therapeutic Department in 1946 he was succeeded by Frank S. Cooksey, O.B.E., M.D., D.Phys. Med., who had ably supported and assisted him in the work of the department since 1934.

EDWARD BELLIS CLAYTON (b. 1882),
M.B., B.Ch., Cantab. (1910)

Bellis Clayton went to Cheltenham College in 1895, thence to Gonville and Caius College, Cambridge, in 1899. He was awarded an Entrance Scholarship in the Medical Department of King's College, London, in 1904. In 1907 he obtained the M.R.C.S., L.R.C.P., and was appointed House-Accoucheur and House Physician to the Children's Department at King's; the next year he was House Surgeon, after which he became Sambrooke Medical Registrar. In 1911 he went to Sweden for a course of study, and on returning to England he turned his attention to the subject of Physio-therapy. In 1912 he was appointed Medical Officer in Charge of the Electrical and Massage Department at King's and in 1913 he became Director of the Physio-therapeutic Department.

During the War of 1914–18 Bellis Clayton became a Captain in the R.A.M.C. and served in the 4th London General Hospital, while retaining the charge of his department at the Hospital (see *King's*, p. 330).

When he retired from King's in December 1946 he was appointed Consulting Physician to the Physio-therapeutic Department. Bellis Clayton is the author of *Medical Gymnastics in Medicine and Surgery, Physio-therapy in General Practice*, and *Some Uses and Abuses of Massage*.

KING'S COLLEGE HOSPITAL AND THE MEDICAL SCHOOL, 1934–1939

1934

THE Hospital Festival Dinner for 1934 was presided over by the Earl of Athlone, and in proposing the toast of King's College Hospital Medical School he referred to the fact that in 1913 there were only 54 students in the Medical School whereas in 1933 there were 349.

During 1934 the Hospital became linked up with two of the London County Hospitals, namely, St. Giles's Hospital, Camberwell, and Dulwich Hospital, East Dulwich Grove.

At St. Giles's Hospital Dr. Henry O. West, an old King's man, had been Medical Superintendent for four years and during that period he established happy relations with King's (see *King's*, p. 323).

At Dulwich Hospital Dr. O. W. Roberts is Medical Superintendent; he, too, is a distinguished old student of King's (see *King's*, p. 345).

1935

The Annual Court was held at King's College on February 27, Dr. W. R. Halliday presided.

The Dowager Viscountess Hambleden and Mr. A. D. Power, the Vice-Chairman, resigned their membership of the Committee of Management. Mr. Power was forthwith elected a Vice-President of the Hospital. He retained the Chairmanship of the Committee which supervises the In-patient Library (see *King's*, p. 420).

The Hon. Edith Smith and Mr. R. A. Hornby joined the Committee of Management, and Cecil P. G. Wakeley was appointed by the Council of King's College to succeed Professor Barclay-Smith as the Council's representative upon the Committee.

Like other institutions honoured by His Majesty King George V as Patron, the Committee of Management of King's offered their loyal congratulations to His Majesty upon the occasion of the Silver Jubilee of his accession to the Throne.

Many patients in the Hospital were enabled to take part in the Jubilee festivities on May 6, through the boon conferred on London Hospitals in 1926 by the *Daily News*, which presented a complete wireless apparatus and earphones for each bed, thus affording the opportunity to listen-in to the broadcast service from St. Paul's Cathedral.

In July H.R.H. the Duke of Connaught relinquished the office of President of the Hospital, which he had held since 1904, when he succeeded the Duke of Cambridge (see *King's*, p. 90).

His great-nephew H.R.H. the Duke of York consented to take his place, and on October 22, at a Special Court held in the Board Room of the Hospital, over which Lord Bayford, one of the Vice-Presidents of the Hospital, presided, the Duke of York was unanimously elected President.

On November 12 the Duke of York visited the Hospital and was given a most cordial welcome by the Chairman and members of the Committee of Management and by many others at 'King's'.

On November 14 at the Hospital Festival Dinner over which the Duke of York presided, Earl Beatty launched the Extension Scheme for the Hospital which included the enlargement of the Nurses' Home, and a new block of wards for private patients, the top floor of which was to be a Maternity Centre and the ground floor equipped as the Dental Department. It was estimated that the cost of these additions would amount to about £110,000.

Early in the year the new X-ray Therapy Sub-department was opened, and later a new Biochemical Laboratory was equipped.

Many changes took place in the honorary staff of the Medical School and Hospital during the year.

Sir Charlton Briscoe, the Senior Physician, resigned and was appointed Consulting Physician to the Hospital and Emeritus Lecturer on Medicine.

Macdonald Critchley was promoted Neurologist, Harold C. Edwards, Surgeon, and William I. Daggett, Surgeon for Diseases of the Ear, Nose, and Throat.

Archibald Gilpin, M.D. Lond., M.R.C.P., was appointed Assistant Physician, Lecturer on Medicine and on Morbid Anatomy.

J. Bell Milne, Thomas W. Widdowson, Walter E. Coe, and John James were promoted Dental Surgeons, and Arthur S. Moore and W. Neville L. Wade were appointed Assistant Dental Surgeons.

Lt. Col. (I.M.S. ret.) Charles H. Barber, D.S.O., M.A., M.D. (see *King's*, p. 310), a former distinguished student of the Medical School, was appointed Lecturer on Tropical Medicine in succession to Professor H. B. Day, who returned to Egypt to take up an appointment there (see *King's*, p. 396).

Sir St. Clair Thomson was elected an Honorary Fellow of the Royal Society of Medicine; and the honour of being appointed a

Chevalier of the Legion of Honour was bestowed upon Sir G. Lenthal Cheatle, K.C.B., C.V.O., by the President of the French Republic; Eustace H. Cluver, M.D., a Burney Yeo Scholar in 1917, was appointed Director of Medical Services in the Union of South Africa (see *King's*, p. 343), and Captain C. F. J. Cropper, I.M.S., became Professor of Physiology in the University of Rangoon (see *King's*, p. 356).

At the M.B., B.S. Examination of the University of London, Joyce M. George was awarded Honours in Obstetrics and Gynaecology, and S. O. Aylett, Honours in Medicine.

The tragic death of Sir Basil Blackett deprived the Hospital of its Deputy Treasurer, an office to which he was appointed in 1934; he was succeeded in office by the Hon. George Colville.

At the Past and Present Students Annual Dinner held on October 5, at which Sir Charlton Briscoe presided, Professor G. Frederic Still was presented by the Chairman with a book containing the names of subscribers to the fund collected for his portrait by Mr. (later Sir) Gerald F. Kelly, R.A., which was exhibited in the Academy that year. Through the generosity of the artist, Mr. Kelly, the proceeds of the portrait fund were devoted to the endowment of a cot in the Children's Ward.

At the conclusion of the year Viscount Hambleden, Patron of King's College Hospital Clubs and Societies' Union, conveyed to the Corporation of King's College Hospital the Sports Ground of over six acres in extent, situated on Dog Kennel Hill, for the use of members of King's College Hospital Medical School.

PROFESSOR ERNEST WILLIAM WHITE, C.B.E. (see *King's*, p. 299).

On November 28 Ernest William White died at Betley House, Shrewsbury. He succeeded Professor Edgar Sheppard (grandfather of the late Canon 'Dick' Sheppard) in the Chair of Psychological Medicine at King's College, London, in 1890. He retired in 1910. Professor White left a legacy to the Medical School to provide for the establishment of 'An annual prize in Psychological Medicine to be known as the "Professor Ernest White Prize", and to be awarded to the most successful student in Psychological Medicine after the theoretical and practical examination'.

1936

On the day of the Royal Funeral in January (His Majesty King George V died on January 20) a largely attended Memorial Service was held in the Hospital Chapel at noon.

Patients and others present in the Out-patients Department had the opportunity of hearing the Service in St. George's Chapel, which was relayed to the Out-patients' Hall.

At the Annual Court of Governors held at King's College on Thursday, February 27, the Principal of the College, Dr. W. R. Halliday, who occupied the Chair, referred to the great loss the Hospital, in common with the Nation, had sustained by the death of its Royal Patron, King George V.

In addition the Chairman referred to the loss the Hospital had suffered in the death of two Vice-Presidents, Mr. Herbert H. Twining (see p. 8) and Lord Forster.

At the same meeting Lord Iliffe was elected a Vice-President of the Hospital.

On March 11 Earl Beatty, Chairman of the Hospital, died. A Memorial Service conducted by the Bishop of Southwark was held in the Hospital Chapel on March 16, at the same time as the funeral service in St. Paul's Cathedral took place.

Later in the year, through the generosity of John Everidge, a copy of a portrait of Earl Beatty was placed in the Board Room of the Hospital (see p. 23). Earl Beatty's memory is also commemorated by a tablet in the vestibule of the Hospital Chapel.

Viscount Hambleden, eldest son of the second Viscount Hambleden, was elected Chairman of the Committee of Management.

Viscountess Hambleden and Sir Reginald Mant, K.C.I.E., were elected members of the Committee of Management: Lord Borodale upon succeeding his father, Earl Beatty, expressed his desire to remain a member of the Committee.

On October 27 the enlarged 'Ear, Nose and Throat' Operating Theatre on the first floor of the Hospital was formally opened by Sir St. Clair Thomson, who before the opening ceremony gave a brief historical retrospect of the development of laryngology and otology.

On November 4 Their Royal Highnesses the Duke and Duchess of York visited the Hospital and were received in the Hall of the Medical School. A Guard of Honour of Nurses was formed under the direction of the Sister Tutor. The occasion was the opening of the completed buildings of the Nurses' Home and the additional accommodation for resident medical officers; also for the reception of purses towards the cost.

In inviting the Duke of York to declare the building open, Viscount Hambleden said 'That a day in the life of a hospital which was entirely devoted to honouring the Nursing Staff was, in my opinion, a day of great importance. Nurses do so much hard work and so often remain in the background! To-day, he continued, I am determined to drag them into full glory of the limelight, and so pay homage to one of the most wonderful callings in the world.'

A vote of thanks to Their Royal Highnesses was proposed by the Dean (Dr. J. A. Drake) and supported by the Sister Matron (Miss M. A. Willcox).

After the ceremony Their Royal Highnesses left the Medical School and made a tour of the new buildings.

During the visit the following officials were presented to Their Royal Highnesses: Viscountess Hambleden (Chairman of the Ladies' Association), Mr. and Mrs. Claud Serocold, Sir Charlton Briscoe, Dr. J. A. Drake, Mr. W. A. Pite (Architect),[1] Miss Willcox, Miss G. L. Buffard (Assistant Matron), Miss K. F. Armstrong (Sister Tutor), and Miss G. M. Matthews (Home Sister).

Their Majesties' visit to King's on this occasion was one of their last public appearances as Duke and Duchess of York.

As a result of the meeting the sum of £3,000 was handed to the Hospital Funds.

Many changes occurred on the staff of the Medical School and Hospital during the year.

H. A. Thomas Fairbank, D.S.O., O.B.E., retired from active work at the Hospital and was appointed Consulting Orthopaedic Surgeon and Emeritus Lecturer on Orthopaedics; Cecil H. M. Hughes, O.B.E., resigned and was appointed Consulting Anaesthetist.

Alan P. L. Cogswell was promoted Anaesthetist and Instructor in Anaesthetics; Hubert Lyon-Cambell Wood became Assistant Orthopaedic Surgeon in addition to his appointment as Assistant-Surgeon.

John H. Peel, B.M., B.Ch., F.R.C.S., M.R.C.O.G., the Chief Assistant in the Obstetric and Gynaecological Department, was appointed Assistant Obstetric and Gynaecological Surgeon; Frederick F. Cartwright was appointed Assistant Anaesthetist and Assistant Instructor in Anaesthetics, and R. E. Clarke, L.D.S., R.C.S., H.D.D. (Edin.), was appointed Dental Radiologist.

The honour of Knighthood was conferred upon Major-General Cuthbert Allan Sprawson, C.I.E., M.D., F.R.C.P., Director-General of the Indian Medical Service (see *King's*, p. 321), and a Commandership of the Royal Victorian Order upon William Gilliatt, M.D., M.S., F.R.C.S., F.R.C.O.G.

---

[1] William Alfred Pite, F.R.I.B.A., Architect of King's College Hospital, Denmark Hill, died in August 1949. He was born in 1860 and educated at King's College School. A Memorial Service to him was held in the Hospital Chapel on 29 August.

At the University of London, Alexander Charles Dalzell was awarded the University Medal at the M.D. Examination, and James Liddell Rossini was awarded Honours in Pathology and Bacteriology at the B.D.S. Examination.

At the Royal College of Physicians Edward Mapother was appointed Bradshaw Lecturer and R. A. McCance, Goulstonian Lecturer.

Professor Sir St. Clair Thomson was awarded the Weber-Parkes Medal and Prize by the Royal College of Physicians for his work on 'Tuberculosis of the Larynx' (see *King's*, p. 410).

PROFESSOR ALBERT CARLESS, C.B.E.

Albert Carless, Consulting Surgeon at King's, who at one time was assistant surgeon to Sir Joseph Lister, died suddenly at Worthing on April 27. During the time that he was in active work at King's he was in all probability the best-known teacher of Surgery in London and by name all over the medical world through his manual of Surgery *Rose and Carless* (see *King's*, p. 389).

PROFESSOR SIR HERBERT JACKSON, F.R.S.

Herbert Jackson, Daniel Professor of Chemistry at King's College from 1914 to 1918, died on December 10 (see *King's*, p. 285).

PROFESSOR WILLIAM BLAIR-BELL

William Blair-Bell, a former distinguished student of King's, died on January 25. At one time he was Professor of Obstetrics and Gynae-cology in the University of Liverpool and Obstetric Surgeon to the Liverpool Royal Infirmary. He left to the Medical School of King's a legacy for the establishment of a Prize in Gynaecology (the Blair-Bell Prize). A 'William Blair-Bell' lecturership to his memory has been established at the Royal College of Obstetricians and Gynae-cologists (see *King's*, p. 311).

In the earlier part of the year Thomas Lambert Lack, J.P., an old King's man, died at the age of 93. He obtained the L.S.A. in 1868 and the M.R.C.S. in 1869. 'Lack of Hingham', widely known in Norfolk, was an excellent exponent of country practice of his time. He was a sound practitioner, a part-time medical officer of health for his district, and a general adviser on sanitation in his neighbourhood.

Shephard T. Taylor, aged 96, died at Edgefield, Norfolk, on August 13. He joined the Medical Department of King's College in 1860.

Shephard Taylor wrote *The Diary of a Medical Student during the Mid-Victorian Period 1860–1864* (see *King's*, p. 163).

Colonel Charles J. W. Tatham, O.B.E., died suddenly in September, at the age of 75. He served in the R.A.M.C. for thirty years. During the War (1914–18) he was Assistant Director of Medical Services, Northern Command, and was awarded the O.B.E. (see *King's*, p. 219).

E. B. Fairweather, M.P.S., F.C.S. (1865–1936), who had retired from the office of Chief Dispenser to the Hospital in 1925, died suddenly on January 25. Fairweather was appointed Assistant Dispenser to Mr. Wilmot at the Hospital in Portugal Street in 1890, and he became Chief Pharmacist in 1897. He was well known to and much respected by King's men, many of whom he had instructed in practical pharmacy. Out of the fullness of his experience he was able to offer valuable suggestions in planning the present hospital Dispensary. He was of great assistance to Professor Frederic Still in preparing successive editions of *King's College Hospital Pharmacopoeia*.

1937

HIS MAJESTY KING GEORGE VI—PATRON

In the early part of the year, H.R.H. the Duchess of Gloucester consented to become President of the Hospital in succession to His Majesty, who ceased to be President on his accession to the Throne. His Majesty King George VI consented to become Patron of King's.

Her Majesty the Queen is great-granddaughter of the Duke of Buccleuch, K.G., who was one of the first Vice-Presidents of King's when the Hospital was inaugurated in 1839, and who was also one of the Vice-Presidents when the Hospital received its constitution by Act of Parliament on August 7, 1851 (see *King's*, p. 37).

The Duchess of Gloucester was formally elected President at the Annual Court held on February 23.

During the year Mr. Claud P. Serocold, O.B.E., retired from the office of Treasurer; he was forthwith elected a Vice-President. Mr. R. A. Hornby was appointed Treasurer and Mr. Edward Hogg joined the Committee of Management.

THE NEW STOCK EXCHANGE WING OF THE HOSPITAL

Mr. Claud Serocold rendered signal service as Treasurer to the Hospital throughout the period 1921–37. It was mainly due to his energy and interest that considerable financial assistance was given to King's by the Stock Exchange Dramatic and Operatic Society, and by other members of the Stock Exchange, particularly by Sir Connop Guthrie, culminating in the formation of a fund amounting to about

£35,000 for the benefit of the Hospital. That amount was utilized towards the cost of the new Stock Exchange Block for Private Patients which was opened by Viscount Wakefield, Vice-President of the Hospital, officially representing His Majesty the King in his capacity as former President of the Hospital, on February 23. At the invitation of Mr. R. B. Pearson, Chairman of the Stock Exchange, Viscount Wakefield unveiled a tablet in the Private Patients' Block bearing the following inscription:

'This tablet records the generosity of the Stock Exchange Dramatic and Operatic Society, through their President, Claud Serocold, Treasurer of the Hospital, and other friends on the Stock Exchange in presenting this Wing for Private Patients.'

The 70-foot tower at the entrance of the Private Patients' Block is a memorial to the flight of Giles Guthrie from England to Johannesburg, and the wording on the tablet in the entrance hall of the Stock Exchange Wing is as follows:

'This tower commemorates the success of Giles Guthrie in the Portsmouth to Johannesburg air race 29.9.36–1.10.36 and his safe return and was erected as a thank-offering by his father, Sir Cannop Guthrie, Bart., K.B.E.'

The Block for Private Patients runs parallel with the main corridors of the Hospital. It contains eighteen single rooms and a Maternity Unit for eighteen patients. The ground floor is equipped for the Dental Department, the transfer of which liberated the Matthew Whiting Ward for in-patients. In the Tower are situated a suite of rooms for the resident medical officer and a room for the safe custody of records.

During the year the Sunlight Department was equipped and an Orthoptic Department established for the treatment of school-children.

The following changes took place in the staff of the Hospital and Medical School during 1937:

Thomas W. Widdowson retired from the Dental Staff and was appointed Consulting Dental Surgeon.

Charles E. Newman was promoted Physician and J. G. Yates Bell promoted Urological Surgeon.

Samuel Nevin, B.Sc., M.D., M.R.C.P., Assistant Physician at the Maida Vale Hospital, was appointed Assistant Neurologist, and Thomas Tennent, M.D., M.R.C.P., D.P.H., D.P.M., Assistant Medical Superintendent at the Maudsley Hospital, was appointed Assistant Physician for Psychological Medicine.

Henry T. Flint, D.Sc. Lond., Ph.D., M.R.C.S., L.R.C.P., was

appointed Consulting Physicist. Aubrey M. Rackow became Senior Assistant Radiologist and Brian G. Thompson, Junior Assistant Radiologist.

Later in the year Harry A. Lucas resigned the office of Vice-Dean, a post which he had held since 1932. He was succeeded by Charles E. Newman.

Towards the end of the year Charles E. Newman resigned his appointments at King's on becoming elected Sub-Dean of the British Post-Graduate Medical School.

At the end of the year John A. Drake, Physician to the Dermatological Department and Dean of the Medical School, retired; he was appointed Consulting Physician for Diseases of the Skin. In the office of Dean he was succeeded by John B. Hunter, M.C.

The Coronation Honours list contained the name of Professor G. Frederic Still, who was awarded the K.C.V.O.

At the University of London Edward Mapother was appointed Professor of Psychiatry; he was also elected a Fellow of University College, London (see p. 113).

At the M.B., B.S. examination Harold W. C. Fuller was awarded the University Medal and honours in Medicine, Pathology, and Surgery, and A. J. Heriot was awarded honours in Pathology. At the University of Cambridge Frank Goldby was awarded the Raymond Horton-Smith Prize (see p. 96).

At the Royal College of Physicians, Group Captain Henry Ashbourne Treadgold, M.D., C.B.E. (1936), Sambrooke Medical Registrar in 1911 (see *King's*, p. 322), and (ret.) Colonel Sydney Smith, M.B., R.A.M.C. (see p. 125), were elected Fellows.

At the Royal College of Surgeons, Cecil P. G. Wakeley was elected a member of the Council, and at the Royal Society of Medicine William H. McMullen was elected President of the Ophthalmological Section (see *King's*, p. 316).

HAROLD WATERLOW WILTSHIRE, D.S.O., O.B.E.

On February 18, 1937, Harold Waterlow Wiltshire died at Bembridge, Isle of Wight. He had been connected with King's since he came down from Cambridge in 1901. He was successively House Surgeon, House Physician, Sambrooke Medical Registrar, Assistant Physician, Physician, and Medical Tutor. He was Vice-Dean from 1919 to 1920 and Consulting Physician to the Hospital since 1925. Wiltshire was the first whole-time Medical Tutor appointed at King's and there is no doubt that he overworked himself in the interest of the Medical School. He left the greater part of his property of the value of £22,481, subject to a life interest, to the Medical School (see *King's*, p. 419).

On April 18 a special service was held in the Hospital Chapel to dedicate the 'Carless Memorial Bed' in Lister Ward, endowed by Mrs. Carless; also as a memorial to Harold W. Wiltshire.

SAMUEL A. KINNIER WILSON

On May 12 Kinnier Wilson, Senior Neurologist, died. He was appointed Assistant Physician for Nervous Diseases and Lecturer on Neurology in the Medical School in 1919 (see p. 88).

SIR JOHN THOMSON-WALKER, O.B.E., D.L.

On October 5 John Thomson-Walker died suddenly at Braeriach, Inverness-shire. He was the first Urologist to be appointed at King's, and during ten years on the honorary staff he took a keen interest in the Hospital and Medical School (see *King's*, p. 411).

On August 17 Mr. G. L. Hawker, who in 1934 succeeded Mr. A. D. Power as Vice-Chairman, died suddenly. He had been a member of the Committee of Management since 1904. His place as Vice-Chairman was taken by the Hon. George Colville, who first joined the Committee in 1922.

The Resident Chaplain, the Rev. Wilfred S. Hatch, after a short illness, died in the Hospital on September 7. He was appointed at King's in 1934 and during the three years of his work he won the respect and affection of those with whom he came in contact. He gave valuable help to many members of the Medical School and in particular to those who belonged to the Hospital Christian Union. He willingly lent the Chapel Vestry for meetings of the Union and he took a real interest in its activities.

Following the death of Mr. Hatch new arrangements were made for the work of the Resident Chaplain; in consequence the Bishop of Southwark resigned his office as Honorary Chaplain. The Rev. Cyril Eastaugh, M.A., Vicar of St. John the Divine, Kennington, the parish to which the Hospital is attached, became Honorary Chaplain and the Rev. C. H. Bostock was appointed Resident Chaplain.

1938

On January 1 John B. Hunter assumed the duties of Dean and A. Wallis Kendall those of Vice-Dean.

On February 1, H.R.H. the Duchess of Gloucester, President of the Hospital, paid her first visit to King's when she was received by Viscount and Viscountess Hambleden, Sister Matron (Miss M. K.

Blyde), and the House Governor (Mr. C. E. A. Bedwell). The Duchess made a tour of inspection of the building and took particular notice of the New Wing of the Nurses' Home, the Chapel, and the Diabetic Kitchen which is part of the unit for the treatment of diabetic patients.

Amongst those who were presented to Her Royal Highness were the Dean (John B. Hunter), the Chairman of the Medical Board (St. John D. Buxton), the Sister Matron (Miss M. K. Blyde), the Assistant Matron (Miss G. L. Buffard), the Sister Tutor (Miss M. I. Otway), the Home Sister (Miss G. M. Matthews), the Sister Housekeeper (Miss M. C. Howell), and the Night Sister (Miss M. Greener).

At the Annual Court held at the Hospital on February 24 Viscount Hambleden, the Chairman, was unanimously elected a Vice-President of the Hospital on completion of ten years' service on the Committee of Management.

Captain the Hon. Henry R. Broughton and Mr. Edwin Strong became members of the Committee.

Later in the year Captain Henry Broughton was appointed the first 'Master of the Garden', so that the gardens of the Hospital might be cultivated to the best advantage within the resources of the Hospital funds.

Early in the year John Clifford Hoyle, M.D. Lond., M.R.C.P., Assistant Physician at Brompton Hospital, was appointed Assistant Physician, and later in the year Thomas Keith Lyle, M.A., M.D., M.Ch. Cantab., M.R.C.P., F.R.C.S., previously an honorary Burney Yeo Scholar and Todd Prizeman in the Medical School, House Physician, House Surgeon, Senior Surgical Registrar, Ophthalmic Registrar, and Chief Assistant in the Neurological Department of the Hospital, was appointed Assistant Ophthalmic Surgeon, and Charles H. Gray, M.Sc., M.B., B.S., A.R.C.S., of University College Hospital, was appointed Biochemist.

In the Hospital the Speech Therapy Department was considerably extended and in the Ophthalmic Department an Orthoptist was appointed.

THE MEDICAL SCHOOL BUILDINGS

A new and up-to-date animal house situated above the Museum Laboratories of the Medical School was opened, the whole cost of which was about £2,800. This addition affords facilities for experimental research work.

This erection completed the new Medical School buildings, the total cost of which was about £47,000. This sum of money had already been found, owing to the generosity of many friends of King's, together with the amount previously reported (see *King's*, p. 367), and with the substantial help from the University of London.

During the year arrangements were made by which all students and resident medical officers are medically examined by one of the physicians of the Hospital once a year or more frequently should the necessity arise. By this means 'breakdowns in health' may possibly be avoided.

At the Royal College of Surgeons, John H. Mulvany was appointed Hunterian Professor for 1939; John V. Dacie was elected to a 'Will Edmonds Clinical Research Fellowship' at K.C.H. J. J. D. King, a former student of the Dental School, was elected to a 'Beit Memorial Fellowship' for a proposed research into dental caries and parodontal disease.

Eustace Henry Cluver was appointed Secretary for Public Health and Chief Health Officer of the Union of South Africa. Previously Cluver was Director of Medical Services of the Union Defence Force and Senior Assistant Health Officer for the Union. Formerly he held the Chair of Physiology in the University of the Witwatersrand (*vide King's*, p. 343). In 1940 Eustace Cluver became appointed Director of the South African Institute for Medical Research in succession to the late Sir Spencer Lister.

At the B.D.S. examination held by the University of London in July C. S. Syms was awarded honours in Pathology and Bacteriology.

During the year a Prize in Tropical Diseases was founded by Mrs. Alec-Tweedie, the authoress, in memory of Professor Sir William Simpson, C.M.G., who was lecturer in Tropical Diseases in the Medical School from 1918 to 1927 (see *King's*, p. 406).

During the International Crisis in the autumn of 1938 arrangements were made whereby the Hospital could be cleared of existing patients and converted into a Civilian Casualty Clearing Station with 1,200 beds. The honorary medical and surgical staff, the resident medical officers, and the students of the Medical School were organized to meet an emergency that might arise. Offers of help came from many former members of the Medical School.

Towards the end of November the Hospital Festival Dinner was held at the Savoy Hotel. Lord Bayford, a Vice-President of the Hospital, occupied the chair in the unavoidable absence of Field-Marshal Sir Philip Chetwode. The combined total received from the appeal at the dinner, together with some donations, amounted to a little over £18,000.

At the end of the year Mr. E. W. Stowe, Clerk to the Hospital, retired after forty years' service. He entered the Hospital in Portugal Street on January 1, 1899, as junior clerk under Mr. John H. Sanders. Mr. Stowe was succeeded in office by Mr. H. T. L. Munro.

SIR RAYMOND H. P. CRAWFURD (see *King's*, p. 393)

Raymond Crawfurd died after a short illness on March 9. He had been a member of the honorary staff since 1898, when he was elected Assistant Physician.

His affection for King's was great and he took a leading part in bringing about the removal of the Hospital from Portugal Street to Denmark Hill. King's owes much to his business and benevolent activities and, in order that his work should be remembered, the Committee of Management decided that one of the Medical Registrarships should bear his name.

When Raymond Crawfurd was House Physician at the Hospital in Portugal Street he was instrumental in inaugurating the K.C.H. Musical Society (see p. 163). In 1925 he was appointed Registrar at the Royal College of Physicians, and he held that office until he died.

In 1915 he was invited to join the Council of Epsom College; he was Chairman of the Epsom College School Committee, 1918–21, Vice-Chairman of the Council, 1921–3, and Chairman, 1923–36. For Epsom College he did much: he wrote scores of letters on its behalf, collected large sums of money, raised the standard of scholarship in the school, planned the biological block, and almost single-handed raised sufficient money to enable the school to build and equip, in 1931, one of the finest sanatoria in the country, the cost of which was £27,000.

Raymond Crawfurd was a regular attendant at Rugby football matches—Twickenham and Blackheath—and he hardly ever missed a Hospital Rugby Football Cup Tie in which King's was engaged. A dramatic finish to the Navy and Army match on March 5 roused him to excitement, an attack of cardiac pain immediately followed, and he passed over calmly four days later.

During the year Louisa Patricia Gordon, M.R.C.S., L.R.C.P. (1923), D.P.H. Camb. (1924), a former student of the Medical School and for some years a Chief Clinical Assistant at the Royal Eye Hospital, died. She left a legacy of £50 to the Medical School.

The death of E. W. Webster occurred in the hospital on July 15th and severed one of the last remaining links with the Hospital in

Lincoln's Inn Fields. Webster commenced his duties at King's on March 4, 1912, as assistant porter in the Operating Theatre where he worked with George Till (see Plate 3). After the removal of the Hospital to Denmark Hill he was transferred to the Morbid Anatomy Department of the Medical School, where he assisted E. C. Sarson. During the War (1914–18) Webster worked for the British Red Cross Society as well as carrying out his duties at King's. When the Pathological Laboratory in the Medical School was opened in 1921, he was appointed Chief Laboratory Assistant and remained at his post until his fatal illness. Webster's early training in the Royal Marines (1906–12) afforded him a due sense of orderliness which made him of great assistance in the development of the teaching side of the laboratory. He had a faculty for remembering faces and names, and many of the past students will call Webster to mind with gratitude for the help which he so often gave to them.

THE CENTENARY APPEAL FUND

A Centenary Appeal Fund Committee was appointed early in 1935 with Mr. Temple C. Twining as its Chairman.

The Centenary Campaign was launched to the public on May 23, 1937, by a broadcast appeal made by Sir Malcolm Campbell, M.B.E., which resulted in the addition of just over £500 to the fund. At the same time press and postal appeals were sent out and these brought in a little over £3,500.

In November of the same year a successful performance of *Macbeth* took place at the 'Old Vic' in Waterloo Road, S.E. The entertainment was organized by the members of the Ladies' Association (see p. 56), and it was attended by Her Majesty the Queen. It realized £1,217 for the Centenary Fund.

In 1938 the Centenary Appeal Committee was reorganized and new members added. Lord Hambleden became President, Lady Hambleden, Chairman, and the new members were the Hon. Edith Smith, Mr. I. J. Pitman, Mr. Harry Tilling, and Mr. V. E. Negus, representing the medical staff.

1939

At the Annual Court of Governors held at the Hospital on February 28, presided over by Viscount Hambleden, the Right Hon. Lord Chatfield, G.C.B., O.M., Admiral of the Fleet, was elected a Vice-President of the Hospital.

Early in the year Rupert Samuel Bruce Pearson, D.M. Oxon., M.R.C.P., of Guy's was appointed Assistant Physician, and it was decided to appoint an additional Medical Registrar, so G. A. Kiloh, M.B., B.S., became Crawfurd Medical Registrar, G. R. Steed, M.B., B.S., continued in office as Sambrooke Medical Registrar, and R. B. Niven, B.M., B.Ch., was appointed Resident Medical Registrar.

During the year a new Diabetic Department was equipped and opened; Robert D. Lawrence, M.A., M.D., F.R.C.P., who seven years previously had been appointed Assistant Physician in charge of the diabetic cases, was appointed Physician-in-charge of the new department, and Wilfrid George Oakley, M.A., M.D. Cantab., M.R.C.P., was appointed Assistant Physician to that department, which is associated with the Biochemical Department of the Medical School. Philip Rainsford Evans, B.Sc., M.B., B.Ch., M.R.C.P., of the University of Manchester, a member of the staff of the Great Ormond Street Children's Hospital, was appointed Assistant Physician to the Children's Department and Leonard Russell Marsh, L.D.S., was promoted Dental Surgeon.

Samuel Nevin, M.D., M.R.C.P., Assistant Neurologist at King's and Director of Research at the Maudsley Hospital, was appointed Professor of Mental Pathology in the University of London.

After seven years in the service of the Hospital, Lewis H. Savin was promoted Ophthalmic Surgeon and Vernon F. Hall promoted Anaesthetist.

In May, Thomas Tennent resigned his appointment as Assistant Physician for Psychological Medicine at King's, upon his election as Medical Superintendent of St. Andrew's Hospital, Northampton. At the end of the summer session Robert A. McCance, Junior Physician and officer in charge of Biochemical Research at King's, resigned his appointment upon his election as Reader in Medicine in the University of Cambridge and Assistant Physician at Addenbrooke's Hospital (see p. 86).

During the year two old King's men, Eric B. Strauss and Geoffrey L. S. Konstam, together with R. S. Bruce Pearson, were elected Fellows of the Royal College of Physicians, and L. Vernon Cargill became Master of the Society of Apothecaries (see *King's*, p. 388).

At the end of March Mr. Cyril E. A. Bedwell, who had been House Governor and Secretary of the Hospital since 1921, indicated that he wished to resign his office in order to take up duties in connexion with the Centenary Appeal; he resumed his seat as a member of the Committee of Management. He was succeeded in office in June by Mr. S. W. Barnes, House Governor and Secretary of the Royal South Hants Hospital, Southampton.

In 1919 Cyril Bedwell was invited to become a member of the

Committee of Management of the Hospital on account of his know-ledge of South London. Previously he held the office of Keeper of Library of the Middle Temple and subsequently he was elected an honorary member of the Inn.

The duties of a chief executive officer of a large hospital have become concerned with matters of policy, and the late Viscount Hambleden (the second) (see *King's*, p. 380), from the position which he occupied in the hospital world, was able to give Mr. Bedwell an exceptional knowledge and breadth of view of hospital affairs. Mr. Bedwell[1] was Deputy Treasurer of the Hospital from 1941 to 1944, and when the Hospital became part of the National Hospital Service in July 1948 and a new Committee of Management was appointed, he was co-opted a member of the Council, the Govern-ing Body of King's College Hospital Medical School.

At the end of July Mr. E. W. Johnston, the Chief Engineer, who commenced his duties at King's on August 1, 1918, retired. His work contributed to many improvements in the Hospital, the chief of which is his sterilizing equipment in the operating theatres.

He was succeeded by Mr. J. Tomlinson, who had held a similar post in the Chesterfield Royal Infirmary.

THE THANKSGIVING SERVICE

On May 12, 1939, the anniversary of the birth of Florence Nightingale (see p. 30), a Service of Thanksgiving to commemorate the centenary of the inauguration of the Hospital was held at St. Paul's Cathedral.

The cathedral was filled and the space beneath the dome was occupied by representatives of the medical and nursing professions, the latter being headed by the Sister Matron, Miss M. K. Blyde, accompanied by Dame Ellen Musson, Chairman of the General Nursing Council for England and Wales.

The Lord Mayor of London (Sir Frank Bowater)—present in state—was assisted by the Bishop of London (Dr. Arthur F. Winning-ton Ingram), and by the Dean of St. Paul's (Dr. W. R. Matthews), also by the Chapter of the Cathedral and by Viscount Hambleden, in receiving the Duchess of Gloucester, President of the Hospital, and Lady Patricia Ramsay, President of the Ladies' Association of King's.

The Bishop of Southwark (Dr. Parsons), attended by the Rev. C. H. Bostock, Resident Chaplain of the Hospital, and the Rev. C. Eastaugh, Chaplain of the Hospital, read the Lessons.

Offerings were made by the Lord Mayor of London on behalf of

---

[1] Cyril Edward Alfred Bedwell died on April 24, 1950.

the Court of Common Council; by former nurses on behalf of the Nurses' League of K.C.H.; by ladies on behalf of the various branches of K.C.H. Ladies' Association; by ladies from the Almoner's Department; by representatives of the K.C.H. Lodge; by the medical and dental students; by the students of King's College, also by representatives of Messrs. W. H. Smith & Son, Ltd. (see p. 9); of Messrs. Twinings, Ltd. (see p. 6); of the South Metropolitan Gas Company, of the Efficiency Club; of the Licensed Victuallers of the Newington Division; of the Brixton and Camberwell Rotary Clubs; of the Westow Philanthropic and Philharmonic Society; of the Waddingtonians (a guild of previous patients of the Anne Waddington Ward), of the Kingfishers (see p. 57), and of the Bun Penny Collectors.

Offerings were also made from the Dulwich College Preparatory School, Mary Datchelor Girls' School, Honor Oak School, James Allen School, the Strand School, and also by private persons.

The gifts were dedicated by the Bishop of London, attended by the Rev. R. V. Galer, formerly Resident Chaplain of the Hospital and supported by the Bishops of Rochester and of Croydon.

The Address was delivered by the Archbishop of Canterbury, who was attended by the Rev. Prebendary R. Hanson, Dean of King's College, London.

During the course of his address the Archbishop referred to the fact that it was on May 13, 1839, that a few laymen and doctors decided to establish a hospital to be attached to the Medical School of King's College and they began by securing the lease of a disused workhouse in Portugal Street. When these humble premises were contrasted with the Hospital on Denmark Hill, which owes so much to William Frederick Danvers Smith, second Viscount Hambleden, there was abundant reason for thanks unto God. Of the advance made in medicine and surgery during the last hundred years, he took as an example the revolution made by Joseph Lister, who held the Chair of Clinical Surgery at King's for fifteen years.

There was special reason to commemorate the revolution in the nursing services, that day being the anniversary of the birth of Florence Nightingale. He ended his address by rendering thanks to God for the blessings bestowed during the last 100 years on King's College Hospital and prayed that it might long keep its honoured place among the great hospitals of London.

Amongst the old King's men present were C. H. East (House Physician in 1885), L. Vernon Cargill (House Surgeon in 1891), H. Willoughby Lyle (House Surgeon in 1894), Sir Charlton Briscoe (House Physician in 1899), John A. Drake (House Surgeon in 1903),

G. de Bec Turtle (House Accoucheur in 1903), and John Everidge (House Surgeon in 1909), all former resident medical officers in the Hospital in Portugal Street, Lincoln's Inn Fields.

Present amongst the members of the nursing staff of the old Hospital were Sisters Caroline A. G. Perkin, Mary A. Peddie, Alice A. Little, and M. A. Willcox, and Nurses J. H. Cole, M. E. Bliss, J. M. Cardoza, F. Hancock, and J. Smales (Mrs. Dawson), together with Mary Gibson, for many years residents' housemaid.

The amount of the offerings received at the service was just over £4,500, which included a gift of one thousand guineas by the members of the staff of Messrs. W. H. Smith & Son, Ltd.

George John Jenkins, O.B.E.

George Jenkins, Emeritus Lecturer on Aural Surgery in the Medical School, died on February 15, 1939. He retired from the post of Director of the Otological Department and Lecturer on Otology at King's in 1932 (see *King's*, p. 400).

Sir Hugh Reeve Beevor, Bt.

Sir Hugh Beevor, Consulting Physician to the Hospital, died in a nursing home near his estate, Hargham Hall, Norfolk, on February 24, at the age of 80. He was Resident Medical Censor at King's College from 1890 to 1893 (see *King's*, p. 336).

For many years Hugh Beevor had been a member of the Court of Examiners at the Apothecaries Hall, London, and he had represented the Society of Apothecaries on the General Medical Council.

He was a recognized authority on forestry and at one time was President of the English Arboricultural Society.

Albert Boyce Barrow

Boyce Barrow, Senior Consulting Surgeon, aged 91, died suddenly in the Prince of Wales Hospital, Tottenham, from injuries received in a motoring accident on May 29.

Barrow retired from the active staff in 1912, but during the War (1914–18), at the request of the Dean, he returned to King's in 1914 so as to assist in the surgical work of the Hospital (see *King's*, p. 268).

Boyce Barrow was born in Newmarket in 1847, so his love of horses, his lifetime hobby and the main interest of his retirement, was acquired early in life. For some years Barrow lived at Writtle, Essex, where he owned horses which were trained under Jockey Club and Pony Turf Club rules and when he had a runner he used to attend the race meeting. His colours, French grey, yellow sleeves, and scarlet cap, were familiar at Northolt. On the day of his fatal accident he had been to Northolt to see a horse of his own breeding—Beguiled —running a good second in the first race of the day.

Boyce Barrow was a man of great personal charm, a kind friend, and a delightful companion. He was full of consideration for others and did not speak unkindly of anybody.

PROFESSOR RALPH PAUL WILLIAMS

Ralph Williams died at his home on May 18. He joined the Medical Department of King's College, London, in 1891 and was the outstanding student and senior scholar of his year (see *King's*, p. 418). In 1914 he was appointed Medical Officer at the Board of Education and in 1934 he became Chief Examiner in Hygiene, which made him responsible for the teaching of hygiene in the Training Colleges.

In 1927 he returned to King's as Lecturer in Hygiene in the Medical School in succession to Professor Sir William Simpson (see *King's*, p. 406). Ralph Williams represented Great Britain at the International Congress on Open-air Education at Brussels in 1931 and at Hanover in 1935. Great as were Ralph Williams's intellectual powers, they were exceeded by his kindness which endeared him to workers in the educational world.

During the year Joseph Henry Philpot, M.B.E., a distinguished old student of King's, Sub-Dean and Medical Tutor, 1874–5, a man of singular intellect, born in 1850, died within three days of his 89th birthday (see *King's*, p. 157).

JOHN ALEXANDER DRAKE (b. 1878), M.D. LOND. (1920), F.R.C.P. (1926), D.P.H. (1919).

John Drake was educated at Malvern College. He entered the Medical Department of King's College, London, in 1896, when he was awarded a Warneford Scholarship. He obtained the Sambrooke Exhibition and Barry Prize in 1897, and in the following year he was Junior Scholar. In 1902 he obtained the M.R.C.S., L.R.C.P., and was appointed House Surgeon to Watson Cheyne. From 1905 to 1915 Drake was in general practice in Tenby, Pembrokeshire, with Dr. Douglas Arthur Reid, an old King's man (see *King's*, p. 318), but during the War (1914–18) he returned to King's and was appointed to the 4th London General Hospital, R.A.M.C. (T.), where later he became Physician-in-charge of the Medical Division (see *King's*, p. 330). In 1919 he returned to the study of Diseases of the Skin and was appointed Clinical Assistant in the Dermatological

Department under the direction of Professor Arthur Whitfield. In 1920 Drake was appointed Assistant Physician in the Dermatological Department and Director of the Department for Venereal Diseases; in 1927 he became Physician-in-charge of his departments. He was appointed Sub-Dean in 1920, Vice-Dean in 1922, and Dean of the Medical School, upon the retirement of Willoughby Lyle, in 1932. He remained Dean until the end of 1937, when he retired from King's and was then appointed Consulting Physician for Diseases of the Skin and Emeritus Lecturer on Dermatology in the Medical School.

CECIL HUGH MYDDLETON HUGHES, O.B.E., M.B., B.S. Lond. (1905), F.F.A., R.C.S. (1948).

Cecil H. M. Hughes was educated at Westminster School and at the Westminster Hospital Medical School. He obtained the M.R.C.S., L.R.C.P., in 1903 and subsequently became House Physician and Resident Obstetric Assistant at the Westminster Hospital.

From 1903 to 1914 he was Administrator of Anaesthetics at the Westminster Hospital, but in 1914 he was appointed Assistant Anaesthetist at King's. Subsequently he became Senior Anaesthetist and Lecturer in Anaesthetics, and when he resigned his appointment in 1936 he was appointed Consulting Anaesthetist.

During the War in South Africa (1899–1901) he was attached to the South African Field Force and served at the Yeomanry Field Hospital; he was actually taken prisoner by de Wet. In 1914 he was appointed Consultant Anaesthetist in the Royal Navy and served with the temporary rank of Surgeon-Commander with Sir Watson Cheyne at the Royal Naval Hospital, Chatham.

Cecil Hughes has also held appointments as Anaesthetist at the Seamen's Hospital, Greenwich, at the Samaritan Free Hospital, at the National Dental Hospital, and at Bethlem Royal Hospital. At the Royal Society of Medicine, Hughes has been President of the section of Anaesthetics.

He has written *Spinal Anaesthesia, Difficulties during Anaesthesia,* and *Anaesthesia in Children.*

PROFESSOR ROBERT ALEXANDER McCANCE (b. 1899), M.A. Cantab. (1925), Ph.D. (1926), M.D. (1929), F.R.C.P. (1935), F.R.S. (1948).

R. A. McCance was educated at St. Bee's School, Cumberland, and saw service during the War (1914–18) as an aeroplane pilot with the Grand Fleet. He went to Sidney Sussex College in 1919 and after taking both parts of the Natural Sciences Tripos in 1922, he worked as a research student in the School of Biochemistry under Sir Gowland Hopkins, O.M., F.R.S.

In 1925 he came to King's, was appointed Demonstrator of Biochemistry, and he obtained the M.R.C.S., L.R.C.P., in 1927. From 1929 to 1932 he held the Pinsent Darwin Research Studentship at Cambridge, while working as Assistant Biochemist at King's, and in 1932 he was appointed Biochemist. In 1930 he obtained the M.R.C.P., and in 1934 he was appointed Junior Physician with charge of Biochemical Research. In 1936 he delivered the Goulstonian Lectures at the Royal College of Physicians in which he reviewed the Medical Problems of Mineral Metabolism.

In 1938 he left King's on his appointment to the newly created Readership in Medicine in the University of Cambridge, where he devotes his time to research and to the direction of Biochemical Research in the Department of Medicine; he was also elected to a Fellowship of Sidney Sussex College, and Honorary Assistant Physician to Addenbrooke's Hospital. Later he became appointed Professor of Experimental Medicine in the University.

McCance is the author of *Experimental Sodium Chloride Deficiency in Man* and he has worked on the Physiology of the Cerebrospinal Fluid.

His contributions to Scientific Medicine, particularly in its biochemical and nutritional aspects, have earned for him a wide reputation. In May 1939 he was appointed a member of the committee on research into problems of preventive medicine.

Miss E. M. Widdowson, Ph.D., who collaborated with him at King's under a grant from the Medical Research Council, continues to work with him in Cambridge.

CHARLES EDWARD NEWMAN (b. 1900), B.A., M.D. Cantab. (1927), F.R.C.P. (1932).

Charles Newman was educated at Shrewsbury School. He served in the Royal Artillery towards the end of the War (1914–18) and went to Magdalene College, Cambridge, in 1919, where he was awarded a scholarship in 1920.

He came to King's in 1921, having been awarded a Medical Entrance Scholarship.

He obtained the M.R.C.S., L.R.C.P., in 1923 and the M.B., B.Ch., in 1924 and was appointed House Physician; subsequently he became Sambrooke Medical Registrar.

In 1926 he gained the Murchison Scholarship at the Royal College of Physicians and took the M.R.C.P. He was appointed Assistant Physician to the Belgrave Hospital for Children in 1929. In 1930 he went for six months to work as Volunteer Assistant to Professor Aschoff in Freiburg, and subsequently was appointed Assistant Physician, Medical Tutor, and Curator of the Pathological Museum at King's.

He delivered the Goulstonian Lectures at the Royal College of Physicians, and was appointed Assistant Registrar there in 1933. In 1937 he became Physician at King's and Vice-Dean of the Medical School, but at the end of the year he was appointed Sub-Dean (and subsequently Dean) of the British Post-Graduate Medical School, and consequently he resigned his other appointments.

Charles Newman was President of the Listerian Society, 1937–8.

He has written papers on the Liver and Gall-Bladder, and a book on *Medical Emergencies*, besides contributing to books on pathology, diagnosis, and treatment.

THOMAS WILLIAM WIDDOWSON (b. 1877), L.D.S. (1900), F.D.S., R.C.S. (1947).

Thomas Widdowson was educated at Liverpool College and at the Liverpool University. He held the post of Lecturer in Dental Anatomy, Physiology, and Dental Histology at King's College, London, during 1924–37.

He was appointed Assistant Dental Surgeon at King's in 1930, Dental Surgeon in 1935, and Consulting Dental Surgeon in 1937.

On the occasion of his retirement from King's, Widdowson was presented with a clock as a token of the high esteem in which he was held by past and present students.

He was President of King's College Hospital Dental Society in 1930 and 1936.

At the University of Liverpool, at the University of London, and at the Royal College of Surgeons, Widdowson has been Examiner in Dental Subjects. As an examiner, he has earned a reputation for sympathy, fairness, and human understanding. He was a member of the Board of Studies in Dentistry at the University of London from 1933 to 1939.

He is the author of *Dental Surgery and Pathology* (1914), *Special Dental Anatomy and Physiology and Dental Histology*, and *The Care and Regulation of Children's Teeth*.

SAMUEL ALEXANDER KINNIER WILSON (1878–1937), M.A., B.Sc., M.D. Edin. (1911), F.R.C.P. (1914).

Kinnier Wilson was educated at George Watson's School, Edinburgh, and at the Edinburgh University where he was awarded the

Gold Medal for the M.D. He was House Physician to Sir Byrom Bramwell at the Edinburgh Royal Infirmary and after finishing that appointment he went to Paris and worked for a year under the inspiration of Pierre Marie. In 1904 he was appointed House Physician to Hughlings Jackson at the National Hospital, Queen Square; later he became the Registrar and Pathologist and was elected to its honorary staff in 1913. When the work at King's was being rearranged in 1919 Kinnier Wilson was appointed Junior Neurologist and Lecturer on Neurology (see *King's*, p. 348). When W. Aldren Turner retired from King's in 1928, Kinnier Wilson became Physician-in-charge of the Neurological Department.

Kinnier Wilson was a neurologist with a philosophic outlook and as a teacher he was held in high esteem. He was Croonian Lecturer at the Royal College of Physicians in 1925 and Morison Lecturer at the Royal College of Physicians, Edinburgh, in 1930.

In 1912 he published a work on *Progressive Lenticular Degeneration* which refers to the possible functions of the corpus striatum. The condition is referred to as 'Wilson's Disease'. He also wrote *Aphasia, Epilepsy and Narcolepsy*, and *Modern Problems of Neurology*. In 1920 he became the first editor of the *Journal of Neurology and Psychopathology* and he remained editor until he died, following an operation, on May 12, 1937.

Names of some of the more distinguished Members of the Medical School from 1934 to 1939

Acton, Iris Ada.
Ainslie, John Archibald.
Alderson, William Edward.
Allardice, Mary Jean.
Allwright, Walter C.
Archer, Nora E. R.
Arkell, E. Douglas.
Austin, Monica H.

Barley, Dennis A.
Barne, Islay Cecil.
Barrett, Melicent E.
Baynes, Alec Hamilton.
Bell, John B.
Beynon, Arthur E.
Binks, Frank A.
Birnie, C. R.
Blackman, Victor.

Bond, Winifred M.
Bradford, Thomas Keith.
Brigden, Wallace W.
Burns, James S. G.
Burrowes, James Taylor.
Bush, Robert J.
Bynoe, Harold Gore.
Bynoe, Raymond W. E.

Campbell, Josephine H.
Cardell, Brian S.
Caton, R. Dennis.
Childs, John Peter.
Clarke, Thomas I. A.
Cleland, Joan.
Comyn, John (M.B.E.).
Conway, Margaret M. J.
Cook, Rosemary Irene.

Copestake, Thomas Neville G.
Crabtree, Norman L.
Crick, Ronald Pitts.
Cronin, Emmanuel.
Cureton, Ronald J. R.
Cutting, Alfred Howard.

Davies, Donald H.
Davis, Geoffrey S.
Dawson, John James Y. (M.C.).
de Launay, Leonard Desmond.
Doel, Geoffrey G.
Duigan, Christina N.
Dunstan, Roy.
Dyer, Gerald F.

Eames, M. E. Hermione.
Edge, Peter A.
Edmondson, Philip W.
Edwards, Joseph R. G.
Eiloart, Mary Elizabeth.
Elias, Minas.
Elphinstone, Roland Henry.
Elsom, Arthur Raymond.
Ethiraj, Fredan Glyn.
Evans, Christopher C.

Fairweather, Donovan J.
Fawcett, Mary Noble.
Filbee, Terence G.
Fisher, Oliver D.

Gee, Beryl M.
George, Joyce M.
Gibson, Dorothy.
Gibson-Hill, Carl Alexander.
Gillieson, Esmé H. M.
Glass, Denis F.
Gray, William M.
Gretton-Watson, Eileen Pearl.
Griffith, Harold G.
Griffiths, Cyril H.
Gunnery, Oswald.

Haigh, Edwin.
Hall, Frederick L.
Halliday, Margaret M. H.
Hamilton, G. E. R.

Harding, Kathleen Mary.
Harrison, Eric J.
Harvey, Claude C.
Hawks, John Christopher.
Helsby, William G.
Henderson, George William D.
Hewlett, Charles R. Floyd.
Hickman, Ursula M.
Horncastle, Charles W. (M.B.E.).
Houghton, Jack Bloor.

Illoway, B. S.

James, C. D. T.
James, Evan Lloyd.
James, Karl G. W.
James, Thomas G. S.
Jarratt, Ernest W.
Jenkins, Gordon T. E.
Johnston, Colin McKie.
Jones, Henry R.
Jones, Hugh Owen.
Jones, James Maxwell.

Kalsy, M. P.
Kennedy, Graeme W.
Kennett, Alexander W.
King, J. J. D.
Kirman, Herbert.
Kitchin, Alfred Philip.

Lattey, Robert Michael.
Levy, Gershon.
Lovel, Raymond William.
Lush, Brandon S.

McColl, Hugh.
Macdonald, Donald G. C.
Mack, Joan.
McKendrick, Jean Dorothy.
McKendrick, Margaret E.
McLaughlin, Margaret E.
Marshall, Terence S.
Mason, Edward T.
Mason, Stanley A.
Maxwell, Violet D.
Micklewright, David.
Millett, Joan S.

Milne, Frank A.
Moir, Raymond A.
Moody, Christine O.
Moore, James D.
Morris, Frederick P.
Morris, John V.
Morris-Wilson, John.
Mulvany, John H.
Murphie, Charles I.

Naish, John M.
Nelson, Maurice P.
Nimalasuria, Ananda.
Niven, Robert Barrie.
Norfolk, Alfred Thomas L.
Norris, Richard L.

Oram, Samuel.
Owen, Ferdinand.

Page, John P.
Palmer, Rowland A.
Parish, Mary P.
Parkinson, Charles Frederick C.
Perredes, John F.
Phillips, Marjorie L. C.
Piggot, Rosa M.
Pitchford, Robert J.
Plews, Peggy Olive Mary.
Price, Bernard Henry.
Price, John E.
Probyn, Thomas C.

Rackow, Aubrey Maurice.
Radcliffe, Douglas W. J.
Reed, W. H. G.
Rees, John E.
Reid, Nora.
Renyard, Harold Homewood.
Richmond, James W.
Ritchie, Douglas A. H.
Roberts, George Barnett.
Robson, Thomas W.
Rossini, James Liddell.
Russell, Arthur Frederick.

Samman, Peter Derrick.
Sandison, Ronald Arthur.

Sandys, Olive Cynthia.
Scholefield, James.
Sell, Charles G. R.
Shaw, Constance M. B.
Sheldon, Alfred John.
Shepperd, Douglas H.
Sherring, Jean Muriel.
Shippard, Stephen G.
Slovick, David.
Small, Michael H.
Smallpeice, John.
Smith, Margaret Joyce.
Speirs, Alastair T. Orr.
Speirs, Robert J. Orr.
Springett, Victor George.
Springett, Victor Henry.
Stalker, Margaret G. S.
Standring, Thomas.
Stark, Ronald B.
Stewart, Cecil Muriel Mary.
Stock, Francis Edgar.
Stockings, George T.
Stoddard, Alan.
Stott, Donald V.
Strong, Frank G.
Syms, Colin Sidney.

Taylor, Edith.
Taylor, Selwyn F.
Todd, John.
Travers, Barbara J.
Truelove, Sidney Charles.
Turner, Anthony Chambers.
Tyson, William J.

Vigar, Charles H.

Waddy, L. H.
Wallace, Alan F.
Waller, Violet E.
Wallis, Hugh R. E.
Warner, Kenneth O.
Warrick, John W.
Watson, John Mortimer.
Webber, Dorothy Joan.
West, Harry Fortescue.
Western, Elizabeth Honor.
Westropp, Celia Kathleen.

Westworth, Ian M.
Wethered, Rodney R. (D.S.C.).
Wheeler, Robert O.
Whetnall, Edith Aileen Maude.
White, Leonard G.
Whitlock, Roy I. H.
Whitteridge, David.
Whittles, James Hill.
Wilbraham, Eric G.
Williams, David Iorwerth.

Williams, Rhys M.
Wilsdon, Kenneth F.
Wilson, A. Bruce Kinnier.
Wilson, John R.
Wood, Keith.
Woollaston, Marion Ethel.

Young, Robert Vincent.
Young, William B.
Young, Winifred F.

GEOFFREY HIRST BATEMAN (b. 1906), M.A., B.M., B.Ch. Oxon. (1930), F.R.C.S. (1933).

Geoffrey Bateman was educated at Epsom College and in 1924 he went to University College, Oxford, having been awarded a Da Silva Exhibition. In 1926 he gained the Theodore Williams Anatomy Prize, and in 1927 he obtained the B.A. with honours in Physiology.

In October 1927 he came to King's, having been awarded an Epsom Scholarship. He obtained the M.R.C.S., L.R.C.P., in 1929 and was appointed House Surgeon in the Ear, Nose, and Throat Department and was Registrar in the same department from 1932 to 1934.

During the six years that he was at King's he was a member of the Lawn Tennis Six; he was Captain in 1929 and in that year he won the Cheatle Cup (see *King's*, p. 479). He also played hockey for King's from 1928 to 1930.

After leaving King's in 1934 he was awarded the George Herbert Hunt Travelling Scholarship of the University of Oxford, when he visited the clinics at Berlin and Zürich.

Geoffrey Bateman became appointed Assistant Surgeon in the Ear, Nose, and Throat Department at St. Thomas's Hospital and Surgeon-in-charge of the Ear, Nose, and Throat Department at the Belgrave Hospital for Children.

He has written on 'Acute Frontal Sinusitis', 'Petrositis', and jointly 'Endaural Approach to Mastoid Process'.

WILLIAM BROWN (b. 1881), M.A., D.M. Oxon. (1918), D.Sc. Lond. (1910), F.R.C.P. (1930).

William Brown was educated at Collyer's School, Horsham, and at Christ Church, Oxford, of which he was a Scholar. In 1906 he was appointed John Locke Scholar in Mental Philosophy. After being an Assistant Master at Bradfield College and later at St. Paul's School, he came to King's College in 1907 and was appointed Lecturer in Psychology in order to assist Professor C. S. Myers in the work of his department. In 1909 he succeeded Myers as head of the department, and in the following year he was awarded the Carpenter Medal for the D.Sc. degree. In 1914 he was appointed Reader in Psychology in the University of London.

William Brown did his clinical work at King's and passed the B.M., B.Ch., in 1914 and obtained the M.R.C.P. in 1921.

Later he was appointed Wilde Reader in Mental Philosophy in the University of Oxford; he was Psychotherapist at King's College Hospital from 1925 to 1931 and Terry Lecturer at Yale University in 1928.

After relinquishing his appointment at King's he was appointed Director of the Institute of Experimental Psychology at the University of Oxford and Consulting Psychologist at the Radcliffe Infirmary. He became Consulting Psychologist and Lecturer on Medical Psychology at Bethlem Royal Hospital.

William Brown has published papers on psychology, some of which are 'Science and Personality'; 'Psychology and Psychotherapy'; 'Suggestion and Mental Analysis'; 'Mind, Medicine and Metaphysics'.

FREDERICK MICHAEL COLLINS, M.A., M.B., B.CH. CANTAB. (1925), F.R.C.S. (1928), COLONEL, I.M.S. (ret.).

Frederick Collins came to King's from Cambridge in 1920 when he was awarded an Entrance Scholarship in Anatomy and Physiology. He obtained the M.R.C.S., L.R.C.P., in 1922 and was appointed Junior Casualty Officer and later House Surgeon in the Urological and in the Orthopaedic Departments.

During the time he was at King's he was a member of the Rugby Football First Fifteen and Secretary of the Club for the seasons 1921–2 and 1922–3.

After leaving King's Collins joined the Indian Medical Service and eventually became Professor of Surgery in the Medical College of Vizagapatam and Madras, Surgeon to His Excellency the Viceroy of India, and Consulting Surgeon to the India Command.

He is the author of *Intussusception from Amoebic Granuloma of the Colon*.

RONALD COVE-SMITH, M.A., M.B., B.CH. CANTAB. (1925), M.R.C.P. (1928), D.P.H. (1931).

Cove-Smith was educated at Merchant Taylors' School, and in 1917 he won an Open Scholarship in Natural Sciences at Gonville and Caius College, Cambridge.

In 1918 he was gazetted as 2nd Lieutenant in the Grenadier Guards, and on demobilization in 1919 he returned to Cambridge. He was in the Cambridge XV in 1919, 1920, and Captain in 1921.

In 1921 he obtained a First-Class in the Natural Sciences Tripos and in the same year he was awarded a Burney Yeo Scholarship at King's. He obtained the M.R.C.S., L.R.C.P., and was Senior Scholar at King's in 1924. He was appointed House Physician in the General Medical Department and later in the Children's Department, and Senior Casualty Officer in 1925. In 1928 he was appointed Sambrooke Medical Registrar and Warden at the 'Platanes' until late in 1929. He has held the post of Registrar at the West End Hospital for Nervous Diseases.

He is Physician-in-charge of the Rheumatic Clinics, Hammersmith, Fulham, and Clapham Park.

Cove-Smith played Rugby Football for England from 1921 to 1929 (see *King's*, pp. 474, 475).

He is the author of *Health for Every Man* (1937).

ALAN WELLESLEY CUBITT (d. 1938), B.M., B.Ch. Oxon. (1927), F.R.C.S. (1932).

Alan Cubitt came to King's from Oxford in 1925 when he was awarded a Burney Yeo Exhibition. In 1926 he became Business Manager of *King's College Hospital Gazette* and Secretary of the Swimming Club.

In 1927 he gained the Tanner Prize, became Senior Scholar, and passed the M.R.C.S., L.R.C.P. He was appointed House Physician in May 1929, and on leaving King's he became House Surgeon at the West London Hospital and later resident medical officer at the Royal Infirmary, Gloucester. Later he became Surgical Registrar at the Middlesex Hospital. In the spring of 1938 he visited Budapest for a course of study, but died suddenly while there.

ALEXANDER CHARLES DALZELL, M.D. Lond. (1936), D.T.M. & H. (1933), D.P.M. (1935).

Alexander Dalzell entered King's College, London, in October 1920 where he was awarded the 'Hare Prize' in Zoology. He joined K.C.H. Medical School in 1923 and obtained the Todd Prize and the M.R.C.S., L.R.C.P., in 1925. The next year he became House Surgeon and in 1927 he passed the M.B., B.S. with distinction in Midwifery and Pathology. He was then appointed Resident Assistant Pathologist at King's.

From 1923 to 1927 Dalzell was a prime mover in the Christmas entertainments at King's, for which he wrote many sketches.

In 1928 he became House Physician at the Ross Institute and Hospital. In January 1929 he went to Honduras and later to Northern Rhodesia to carry out investigations on malaria for Sir Malcolm Watson, M.D., Principal of the Malaria Department and Director of the Ross Institute of Tropical Hygiene. In 1933 Dalzell was appointed Medical Officer in the West African Service and went to Sierra Leone.

In 1934 he returned to England and engaged in the study of Mental Diseases and in January 1936 he obtained the M.D. in Psychological Medicine and was awarded the University Medal.

Alec Dalzell is an artist of repute and during the last ten years he has exhibited pictures in provincial galleries and at the Royal Academy in 1935, 1936, and 1939 ('The Auda Valley' 186, a landscape of originality).

In 1938 he was appointed First Assistant Medical Officer at Banstead Hospital; in 1940 he became Deputy Medical Superintendent at the L.C.C. Hospital, Caterham, and later Medical Superintendent of the Frian Hospital, New Southgate.

PROFESSOR FRANK GOLDBY, (b. 1903), M.D. Cantab. (1936), M.R.C.P. (1928).

Frank Goldby was educated at the Mercers' School and Gonville and Caius College, Cambridge, which he entered in 1920. He obtained a First-Class in the Natural Sciences Tripos Part 1 and Part 2. At Cambridge he was awarded a College Scholarship, the Tancred Studentship, and was Frank Smart Research Student (1923–4).

He came to King's in 1924 and was awarded the Senior Scholarship and the Todd Prize for Clinical Medicine in 1926, and in the same year he obtained the M.R.C.S., L.R.C.P. He was appointed House Physician and later Resident Clinical Pathologist at King's.

He obtained the M.B., B.Ch. of Cambridge in 1928 and was appointed House Physician at the Ross Institute, Putney, after which he returned to King's and was Assistant Clinical Pathologist (1929–30).

He then went to University College, where he was Senior Demonstrator of Anatomy from January 1931 to July 1932. His next appointment was that of Lecturer-in-charge of the Anatomical Department at the University of Hong Kong. He returned to Cambridge in 1933, where he was appointed Demonstrator and later Lecturer in Anatomy in the University and a Fellow of Queens' College.

In 1936 he was awarded the Raymond Horton-Smith Prize for his M.D. Thesis and in 1937 he was appointed to the Elder Professorship of Anatomy and Histology in the University of Adelaide. In 1945 he returned to England and was appointed Professor of Anatomy in the London University, at St. Mary's Hospital Medical School.

Frank Goldby has published papers on Embryology and on the 'Pathology and Comparative Anatomy of the Nervous System'.

FREDA KATHARINE HERBERT, M.A. Cantab., M.B., B.S. Lond. (1925).

Freda Herbert was educated at Oxford High School and at Girton College, Cambridge, where she was a scholar. She obtained a First-Class in the Natural Sciences Tripos in 1922, and came to King's in October of the same year. In 1924 she obtained the Tanner Prize and in the following year obtained the M.R.C.S., L.R.C.P., and the M.B., B.S.

She was appointed Assistant Casualty Officer at King's and worked in the Pathological Department. After leaving King's she was appointed Assistant Pathologist at the Belgrave Hospital for Children. From 1926 to 1930 she was engaged in research work in Chemical Pathology in association with Geoffrey A. Harrison (see *King's*, p. 344) at the Hospital for Sick Children, Great Ormond Street, and at St. Bartholomew's Hospital.

In 1930 she was appointed Biochemist to the Royal Victoria Infirmary, Newcastle-on-Tyne, and Demonstrator (later Lecturer) in Pathological Chemistry in the University of Durham College of Medicine, now the Medical School, King's College, Newcastle, University of Durham.

Freda Herbert has published numerous papers on biochemical subjects in the *Biochemical Journal*, the *British Journal of Experimental Pathology*, and in the *British Medical Journal*.

DORIS ELEANOR PARKER JOLLY, M.B., B.S. Lond. (1921), D.P.H. (1922), M.M.S.A. (1932).

Doris Jolly joined the Medical Faculty of King's College, London, in 1917 and was actually the first woman student to be admitted to King's College Hospital Medical School when it was opened to women in May 1918.

She was awarded the Tanner Prize in 1919 and became Senior Scholar in 1920, the same year in which she passed the M.R.C.S., L.R.C.P. She then became appointed House Accoucheur.

After leaving King's she was appointed resident medical officer at the Wolverhampton General Hospital, and in 1923 she entered the Public Health Service. In 1932 she obtained the Mastership of Midwifery of the Society of Apothecaries (see *King's*, p. 375). She became Senior Maternity and Child Welfare Medical Officer and later Assistant M.O.H. at Ipswich.

GAVIN HAMILTON LIVINGSTONE, M.B., B.S. LOND. (1929), F.R.C.S. (1930).

Gavin Livingstone received his earlier education at King's College, London. He entered K.C.H. Medical School in 1924 and obtained the M.R.C.S., L.R.C.P., in 1926. He was appointed House Surgeon in 1927 and later House Surgeon to the Ear, Nose, and Throat Department. From 1928 to 1929 he was Senior Casualty Officer.

In 1930 he was appointed Bernhard Baron Research Scholar in Oto-Rhinology at the Middlesex Hospital, but in 1931 he returned to King's on being elected Registrar in the Ear, Nose, and Throat Department.

From 1932 to 1933 he had a Geoffrey E. Duveen Travelling Studentship in Oto-Rhinology, and from 1933 to 1935 was Registrar in the Ear, Nose, and Throat Department at the Middlesex Hospital.

During the time Gavin Livingstone was at K.C.H. he was awarded his First Fifteen Colours and in 1924 he was in the team which won the Junior Inter-Hospitals Cricket Cup.

He became Assistant Surgeon at the Golden Square Hospital, Surgeon-in-charge of the Throat Department at the Metropolitan Hospital, and Aural Surgeon at the Bolingbroke Hospital. Later he went to Oxford and became appointed Assistant Aural Surgeon at the Radcliffe Infirmary.

RONALD GRAEME MACBETH, M.A., D.M., OXON. (1950), F.R.C.S. ED. (1933).

Ronald Macbeth came to King's from Oxford in 1926 when he was awarded a Burney Yeo Scholarship. When the Medical School Sports were inaugurated in 1928 he was appointed Captain, and in 1931 he represented King's in the 440 yards at the United Hospital Athletic Sports.

He obtained the M.R.C.S., L.R.C.P., and his Oxford Degree in 1928; he was then appointed House Surgeon to the Ear, Nose, and Throat Department and later House Surgeon at King's. In 1930 he was awarded the George Hunt Travelling Scholarship by the University of Oxford and later he became Honorary Surgeon to the Ear, Nose, and Throat Department of the Radcliffe Infirmary, Oxford.

H

EDMUND CLAUD MALDEN, *C.V.O.* (1941), M.B., B.CH. CANTAB. (1924).

Edmund Malden was educated at Tonbridge School, from which he went to Gonville and Caius College in 1909, having been awarded a Tancred Studentship. He took the Natural Sciences Tripos in 1912, and came to King's in 1913, having gained an Entrance Scholarship in General and Clinical Pathology. He obtained the M.R.C.S., L.R.C.P., in 1915 and almost immediately obtained a temporary commission as Captain in the R.A.M.C. He served in France with the 12th Division from May 1915 to June 1919. He returned to King's in 1919 and was appointed House Surgeon; later he was House Physician in the Children's Department. In April 1920 he went into practice at Windsor and eventually was appointed Physician and Pathologist to King Edward VII Hospital, and Medical Officer to the Imperial Service College, Windsor.

In 1938 Edmund Malden was appointed Surgeon-Apothecary to His Majesty's Household at Windsor Castle in succession to Sir Henry L. Martyn who resigned (see *King's*, p. 317).

LUDLOW MURCOTT MOODY, M.D. LOND. and M.R.C.P. (1919), D.T.M. and HY. (1922), A.K.C. (1920).

L. M. Moody joined the Medical Faculty of King's College, London, in 1913, when he was awarded a Warneford Entrance Scholarship. At the College he gained the Warneford and the Leathes Prizes, the Huxley Prize in Physiology, and became Second-Year Scholar.

He came to King's College Hospital in 1916 when he was awarded the University Entrance Scholarship. In 1918 he became Senior Scholar and won the Todd and the Tanner Prizes, and in the same year he passed the M.R.C.S., L.R.C.P., and the M.B., B.S. Lond. At King's he held the appointment of Assistant Bacteriologist in the Pathological Laboratory.

After leaving King's, Moody returned to Jamaica, where he was appointed the Government Bacteriologist.

He is the co-author of *Alastrim in Jamaica* (1921).

GEORGE HENRY NEWNS, M.D. LOND. (1933), M.R.C.P. (1932).

George Newns received his earlier medical education at King's College, London. He obtained the M.B., B.S., in 1931 and was appointed House Physician, and in 1934 he became Registrar to the Children's Department at K.C.H.

He was awarded the Murchison Scholarship by the Royal College of Physicians in 1932. After leaving King's he held the appointments of Medical Registrar at the Royal Northern Hospital, House Physician and later Medical Registrar at the Hospital for Sick Children, Great Ormond Street. He is Physician to the Bolingbroke Hospital and Physician to the Queen Elizabeth Hospital for Children, London.

He is author of 'Mandelic Acid in the Treatment of Pyelitis in Children' and 'Extreme Leucocytosis in Whooping-Cough' (*Lancet*).

HENRY ALEXANDER OSBORN (1893–1937), M.A., D.M. Oxon. (1935), D.P.H. (1923).

Henry Osborn was born in Ladysmith; he was educated at Pietermaritzburg College and at the University of Natal, where he obtained the B.A. and was awarded a Rhodes Scholarship. In 1917 he took up his Scholarship at New College, Oxford. He came to King's in 1919 when he was awarded a Scholarship in General and Clinical Pathology. While at King's he played hockey and lawn tennis for the Hospital.

He obtained the M.R.C.S., L.R.C.P., in 1921 and also took the B.M., B.Ch., in 1922 and was appointed Junior Casualty Officer and later Resident Clinical Pathologist. In 1928 he became Pathologist to the King Edward Memorial Hospital, Ealing, and Consulting Pathologist to the Wembley Hospital. In 1932 he was appointed Pathologist to the Southern Group of Municipal Hospitals of the City of Liverpool where he organized the pathological service. While at Liverpool he conducted research on Pemphigus Neonatorum and initiated successful treatment.

In the course of his work at Liverpool his thumb became infected while he was conducting a post-mortem examination; he contracted septicaemia and died on January 23, 1937.

Osborn was an ideal clinical pathologist, spending his time between the wards, the laboratory, and the post-mortem room, integrating pathology with clinical work, to the great advantage of the patients and his colleagues.

KEREN ISABEL PARKES, M.D. Lond. (1931), F.R.C.S. (1932), A.K.C. (1929).

Keren Parkes joined the Medical Faculty of King's College, London, in 1924 when she was awarded a Warneford Entrance Scholarship. She gained the Rabbeth Medical Scholarship, the Second-Year Scholarship and Warneford Prize, the Alfred Hughes Prize in Anatomy, and the Jelf Medal for Intermediate Medical Subjects.

She came to the Hospital in October 1926, and was Secretary of the Women's Hockey Club for the season 1927–8, Captain in 1929, and Secretary of the Women's Common Room.

She was awarded the Burridge Prize, the Jelf Medal, and the Todd Prize.

Keren Parkes obtained the M.R.C.S., L.R.C.P., in 1928 and the M.B., B.S., in the following year. She was appointed Obstetric and Gynaecological House Surgeon in 1929 and during 1930 to 1932 she was Sambrooke Obstetric Registrar and Tutor (see *King's*, p. 375). After leaving King's she became Surgical Registrar at the Elizabeth Garrett Anderson Hospital from 1933 to 1935, and Resident Obstetrician at the Kingston and District Hospital, 1936–7. She holds the appointment of Antenatal Officer for the Surrey County Council.

PATRICK HERBERT LYON PLAYFAIR, M.A., M.D. CANTAB., F.R.C.S. (1933), M.R.C.O.G. (1936).

Patrick Playfair came to King's from Caius College, Cambridge, in 1926. He was soon elected Secretary of K.C.H. Rugby Club and of the Listerian Society. He obtained the M.R.C.S., L.R.C.P., in 1928 and the M.B., B.Ch., in 1932. He was appointed House Surgeon and Obstetric and Gynaecological House Surgeon at King's in 1929. He was resident medical officer at Hillingdon County Hospital 1931–2, and later Accoucheur under Professor Couvelaire at the Clinique Baudeloque in Paris. In 1934 he was appointed resident medical officer at Queen Charlotte's Hospital, after which he went to the United States and worked in an Obstetric and Gynaecological Clinic at Detroit and Chicago. In 1935 he was appointed Obstetric Registrar and Tutor at Queen Charlotte's Hospital, and Obstetric and Gynaecological Registrar and Tutor at King's.

In 1937 Patrick Playfair was appointed Honorary Assistant Gynaecological and Obstetric Surgeon at the Royal Hospital and at the Women's Hospital, Wolverhampton. He also became Honorary Gynaecologist at the Guest Hospital, Dudley.

He is the author of *Acetylcholine in the Treatment of Uterine Inertia* and of other gynaecological articles.

EDWARD JOHN SOMERSET, M.S. LOND. (1938), D.O.M.S. (1936), MAJOR, I.M.S.

John Somerset obtained the M.R.C.S., L.R.C.P., in 1932 and the M.B., B.S., in 1934. At King's he became House Surgeon, House Physician, and Ophthalmic House Surgeon. Later he was appointed Ophthalmic Registrar, and while holding that office he worked at the Royal Eye Hospital where he was Research Scholar; after that appointment he obtained the M.S. London in Ophthalmology. In 1927 John Somerset was included in the team which represented King's in the United Hospital Sports; the team obtained second place to the London Hospital (see *King's*, p. 470).

He was Secretary of the Listerian Society for the session 1931-2.

John Somerset became Professor of Ophthalmology at the Medical College, Calcutta. He is the author of *Modification of Bowman's Lachrimal Probes* and *Incidence of Refractive Errors in Blepharitis of Children*.

ERIC BENJAMIN STRAUSS (b. 1894), M.A., D.M. Oxon. (1930), F.R.C.P. (1939).

Eric Strauss was educated at Oundle School and at University College School. During the War (1914-18) he was Captain in the Infantry at home and in the field. In the Michaelmas Term 1918 he entered New College, Oxford, and joined the Medical School at King's in October 1921. He obtained the B.M., B.Ch., in 1924 and was appointed House Physician in 1925; in the same year he became House Physician at the Hospital of St. John and St. Elizabeth. He was Senior Medical Registrar at the Hospital for Epilepsy and Paralysis, 1926-9, and during part of that period he worked at the Maudsley Hospital. For a time he was Assistant Physician at Marburg University Hospital for Mental and Nervous Diseases under Professor Kretschmer, and Clinical Research Assistant in the Department of Psychological Medicine at Guy's.

He was Assistant Physician at the Cassell Hospital, Penshurst, for Functional Nervous Diseases from 1931 to 1934, when he was appointed Physician at the Tavistock Clinic (Institute of Mental Psychology). In 1938 he became Physician for Psychological Medicine at St. Bartholomew's and Lecturer in Psychological Medicine at St. Bartholomew's Hospital Medical School.

Eric Strauss has written *Recent Advances in Neurology and Neuro-Psychiatry* (with W. Russell Brain); a *Textbook of Medical Psychology*; *Hypnotism*; *Sexual Disorders in the Male* (with Kenneth Walker); and *Psychogenic Asthma*.

DICK BRASNETT SUTTON, M.B., B.S. Lond. (1924), F.R.C.S. Ed. (1930), D.L.O. (1928).

Dick Sutton came to King's in 1920 and from the first took a keen interest in the Hockey Club. He played regularly from 1920 to 1924, and during most of that time he was the energetic Secretary and mainstay of the Club. During 1921–2 he managed two teams; during 1922–3 he managed three teams; and during 1923–4 he managed four teams. During these periods, and mainly owing to his energy, King's twice reached the Final Inter-Hospitals Hockey Cup-tie.

Dick Sutton obtained the M.R.C.S., L.R.C.P., in 1922 and was appointed House Surgeon at King's; during the next year he was House Surgeon in the Ear, Nose, and Throat Department, and for another year he remained Clinical Assistant in that department.

Dick Sutton became appointed Honorary Aural Surgeon to the Chepstow and District Hospital, and Honorary Surgeon in the Ear, Nose, and Throat Department at the Royal Gwent Hospital.

He is the author of 'A Case of Gradenigo's Syndrome', *British Medical Journal* (1929).

GEOFFREY FAUSITT TAYLOR, M.A., M.B., B.Ch. CANTAB. (1925), M.R.C.P. (1931), LIEUT.-COLONEL, I.M.S. (ret.).

Geoffrey Taylor entered K.C.H. from Sidney Sussex College, Cambridge, in 1923. During the time he was at King's he was a member of the Rugby First Fifteen. 'A very sound player who trains hard and plays hard. He is always on the ball and is good both in attack and defence.'

He passed the M.R.C.S., L.R.C.P., in 1925 and was appointed House Physician and later House Surgeon.

After leaving King's Geoffrey Taylor joined the Indian Medical Service; he eventually became Professor of Medicine in King Edward Medical College, Lahore, and Consulting Physician, 14th Army and Eastern Command, India.

FRANCIS WILFRED WILLWAY (1908–44), B.Sc., M.D. LOND. (1934), M.S. (1933), F.R.C.S. (1932), A.K.C. (1928).

Wilfred Willway entered the Medical Faculty of King's College, London, as a Warneford Scholar in 1924. He was awarded the Leathes Prize, Barry Prize, Alfred Hughes Memorial Prize, and the Huxley Prize. He graduated B.Sc. Lond. with honours in 1928. He joined the Hospital Medical School and gained the Tanner Prize and the Jelf Medal, and obtained the M.R.C.S., L.R.C.P., in 1930. In 1931 he was appointed Resident Casualty Officer and at the conclusion of the appointment he became Senior House Surgeon at the Royal East Sussex Hospital and later Resident Surgical Officer at the Royal Manchester Children's Hospital. He returned to King's and became Surgical Registrar and Tutor. Early in 1936 he was appointed Honorary Assistant Surgeon at the West End Hospital for Nervous

Diseases, but later in the year he became Surgical Registrar at the Bristol Royal Infirmary.

Although affected by indifferent health Wilfred Willway devoted himself whole-heartedly to the study of Neuro-Surgery. He became Assistant Surgeon to the Bristol Royal Infirmary and to the Bristol General Hospital. During the early period of the War (1939–45) he was E.M.S. Specialist to the Neurosurgical centre at the Burden Neurological Institute, Bristol.

Wilfred Willway was one of the first neuro-surgeons to employ Walter Freeman's modification of Moniz's operation of prefrontal leucotomy (1936); he described his technique in his Hunterian Lecture at the Royal College of Surgeons in 1942.

There is no doubt that Wilfred Willway exhibited a true scientific approach to medical problems. He died after a protracted illness in January 1944.

JOHN CASPER WINTELER (b. 1910), M.D. Lond. (1935), M.R.C.P. (1935), A.K.C. (1934).

John Winteler was educated at Whitgift School and at King's College, London, which he entered in 1928, when he was awarded a Warneford Entrance Scholarship. At the College he obtained the Barry Prize and the Warneford Prize, and at King's College Hospital the Todd Prize and the Jelf Medal. In 1933 he obtained the M.R.C.S., L.R.C.P., and the M.B., B.S.

After holding the appointments of House Physician in 1934 and House Physician in the Children's and Neurological Departments, 1934–5, he was appointed Sambrooke Medical Registrar, becoming Senior Medical Registrar in 1937.

For a period he was Physician to the Belgrave Hospital for Children, but in 1939 he obtained the appointment of Medical Officer to the Ministry of Health.

Winteler is the author of *The Treatment of Jaundice in Children*.

SECTION VIII

KING'S COLLEGE HOSPITAL AND THE MEDICAL SCHOOL DURING THE PERIOD OF THE WAR
1939 to 1945

WHEN war was declared on Sunday, September 3, 1939, King's was already organized and became immediately mobilized as Sector Number IX (K.C.H. Sector) of the Ministry of Health's Emergency Medical Service for London, under the general direction of John B. Hunter, M.C., the Dean and Surgeon to the Hospital, as Chief Medical Officer, and Terence Cawthorne, Vice-Dean and Surgeon for Diseases of the Ear, Nose, and Throat, as Deputy Chief Medical Officer, with the House Governor, S. W. Barnes, as Lay Officer, and the Sister Matron, Miss M. K. Blyde, as Matron.

The K.C.H. Sector, somewhat triangular in shape, with headquarters at Horton Emergency Hospital, Epsom, stretched from Camberwell Green at the apex to Horsham and Haywards Heath at the angles. It also included the hospitals at Dulwich, Croydon, Horton, Leatherhead, and Redhill. King's College Hospital became primarily a large casualty clearing station, supplemented by a first-aid post, as one of the units of the local organization.

An emergency operating theatre was constructed in a protected part of King's; the accommodation for maternity patients, general and private, remained, and members of the Hospital staff and of the Medical School were available to attend mothers in their own homes.

At King's College Hospital Bruce Pearson became Resident Physician and Harold C. Edwards, for a short time, was Resident Surgeon. Later Arthur Edmunds, C.B., Consulting Surgeon to King's, who had retired from his honorary staff appointment in 1934 (see *King's*, p. 396), returned to assist in the surgical work of the Sector IX at Cuckfield E.M.S. Hospital in Sussex, and H. A. Thomas Fairbank, D.S.O., O.B.E., who had retired from his honorary staff appointment at King's in 1936, became Consulting Adviser in Orthopaedics to the Emergency Medical Service; later he became Honorary Consultant in Orthopaedics to the Army.

The following members of the medical staff of King's joined H.M. Forces:

The Royal Navy

Cecil P. G. Wakeley became Surgeon Rear-Admiral and Consulting Surgeon to the Navy.

Macdonald Critchley, Surgeon-Captain, R.N.V.R., and Consultant in Neurology.

A. Wallis Kendall, Surgeon-Captain, R.N.V.R., on duty with the Pacific Fleet.

The Army

St. John Dudley Buxton became Brigadier, R.A.M.C., Consultant in Orthopaedic Surgery, M.E.F.

Harold C. Edwards, Brigadier, R.A.M.C., Consultant in Surgery, C.M.F.

W. I. Daggett, Brigadier, R.A.M.C., Consultant in Oto-Rhino-Laryngology, G.H.Q., India.

E. Grainger Muir, Colonel, R.A.M.C., M.E.F.

Hugh W. Davies, Lieut.-Col., R.A.M.C., Adviser in Radiology, S.E.A.C.

Vernon F. Hall, Brigadier, R.A.M.C., Adviser in Anaesthetics, S.E.A.C.

Samuel Nevin, Lieut.-Col., R.A.M.C., Adviser in Neurology, S.E.A.C.

The Royal Air Force

T. Keith Lyle, Air-Commodore, R.A.F.V.R., Consultant in Ophthalmology, overseas.

J. Myles Bickerton, Wing-Commander, R.A.F.V.R., Ophthalmic Specialist.

1940

In January 1940 and subsequently the students in the Medical School were arranged in three main groups for their clinical work: the first-year 'final' students went to the Leatherhead Emergency Hospital, the second-year 'final' students, to the Horton Hospital, and the third-year 'final' students to King's. Some of the students attended other hospitals for special courses of instruction.

At the Annual Court held on March 14 at the Savoy Hotel and presided over by Mr. A. Danvers Power (see *King's*, p. 420), the Earl of Clarendon, K.G., G.C.M.G., G.C.V.O., was elected a Vice-President of the Hospital.

Later in the year Viscount Hambleden appealed for 'Centenary Gifts' for the Hospital. He indicated that under the prevailing war conditions it was not possible for the Centenary Appeal Fund Committee to organize entertainments in support of the fund with any degree of success.

On June 6 Her Royal Highness, the Duchess of Gloucester, the

President of the Hospital, went to King's. She made a tour of the building and displayed particular interest in the emergency arrangements.

In November Charles W. M. Hope retired from the active staff of the Hospital after twenty-seven years of service; he was appointed Consulting Surgeon to the Ear, Nose, and Throat Department (see p. 112).

THE NEW DENTAL DEPARTMENT

In December 1940 the New Dental Department, which occupies the ground floor of the Stock Exchange Wing of King's, was formally opened by Sir Frank Pearce.

The new department includes a conservation room equipped with thirty-five chairs and units, a children's department with nine chairs and units, a lecture theatre, a demonstration room, an X-Ray room, a phantom-head room, a prosthetic room for providing dentures, a laboratory, and administrative offices.

The cost of the department was met by the Trustees of the late Alexander Bohrmann, a near neighbour of King's, also by a grant of £2,000 from the Dental Board of the United Kingdom.

In January 1941 J. J. D. King, L.D.S., Ph.D. Sheffield, was appointed temporary Assistant Dental Surgeon and Archibald H. Galley, M.B., B.S., D.A., a former Rabbeth Scholar in the Medical School, was appointed Assistant Anaesthetist to the Dental Department.

On March 20 Professor Edward Mapother died after a long illness; his death removed an outstanding figure from English Psychiatry. The friendly co-operation between King's and the Maudsley Hospital was accomplished largely through his influence (see p. 113).

Colonel George W. Shore (b. 1888) died on May 8 at Charing Cross Hospital. When war was declared, part of the Middlesex County Mental Hospital at Shenley was taken over by the Military Authorities, and George Shore, Medical Superintendent of the Hospital and Lieut.-Colonel in the Territorial Army Reserve, assumed command (see *King's*, p. 320).

On September 10 Professor R. T. Hewlett died at Greenwich. He had lived through the golden age of bacteriology of which he became a master, but his leaning was, for the most part, towards public health (see *King's*, p. 283).

1941

In the New Year's Honours Surgeon Rear-Admiral Cecil P. G. Wakeley was awarded the C.B. (Military) and Edmund C. Malden,

Surgeon-Apothecary to H.M. Household at Windsor, a former Pathology Scholar in the Medical School, was awarded the C.V.O.

On March 20 Her Royal Highness the Duchess of Gloucester again visited the Hospital and was received by Viscount and Viscountess Hambleden. The Duchess visited the wards and talked with many of the patients.

At the London University Samuel Oram, a distinguished student of the Medical School, was awarded the University Medal at the M.D. examination.

On June 28 Sir Frederic Still, K.C.V.O. (1937), Physician Extraordinary to H.M. the King, died at Harnham Croft, Salisbury (see *King's*, p. 408). His Majesty was represented by Colonel the Hon. Sir George Herbert at the funeral service at Salisbury Cathedral on July 3.

On April 3 Colonel T. Boswell Beach died at Reading. He was House Physician at King's in 1890. Boswell Beach was a man who went through life contributing to the happiness of others, largely by his courteous manner and good humour (see *King's*, p. 219).

On September 15 Group-Captain Henry A. Treadgold died. He was Consultant in Medicine in the R.A.F.; he received the C.B.E. in 1936 and became F.R.C.P. in 1937 (see *King's*, p. 322).

On November 20 Henry O. West (b. 1885), Medical Superintendent of Queen Mary's Hospital for Children at Carshalton, died. In 1909 he was House Surgeon to Albert Carless at King's. Henry West became an authority on non-pulmonary tuberculosis in children and at one time he was Tuberculosis Officer for Kent. He was elected F.R.C.P. in 1936 (see *King's*, p. 323).

On December 4 Godfrey de Bec Turtle (b. 1877) died at the Luton and Dunstable Hospital to which he had gone to superintend the work during the war (see *King's*, p. 322).

1942

Lectures on Industrial Medicine were delivered at the Medical School, and visits to a large factory were arranged and demonstrations held. The course comprised the treatment of accidents and of illnesses which occur in industry and the laws which relate thereto.

During the year Alan P. L. Cogswell, Barrister-at-Law, Gray's Inn, retired from the post of Anaesthetist to the Hospital upon being appointed H.M. Coroner for the Eastern District of the County of Middlesex; however, he retained the lectureship in Forensic Medicine. Alan Cogswell was appointed Junior Anaesthetist in 1929, Lecturer in Anaesthetics to the Dental School in 1930, and Lecturer in Forensic Medicine and Toxicology in the Medical School in 1933.

On June 29 William D. Sturrock (b. 1880), D.S.O., a former House Surgeon at King's, died. Before he came to King's in 1903 he had been at Charterhouse and later at Magdalen College, Oxford. When he left King's he went into practice with Walter T. Brooks in Oxford (see *King's*, p. 204), and later he became one of the original Medical Officers of the Maternity Department of the Radcliffe Infirmary, Oxford. Throughout his life Sturrock's work was a model of diligence and of close attention to detail (see *King's*, p. 321).

1943

On January 29 Professor Sir St. Clair Thomson died in Edinburgh as the result of an accident. At the meeting of the Section of Laryngology of the Royal Society of Medicine held on November 4, 1932, Sir St. Clair Thomson was presented with his portrait in oils by members of the section. He had been Throat Physician to King Edward VII. In 1935 St. Clair Thomson was elected an Honorary Fellow of the Royal Society of Medicine (see *King's*, p. 410).

On November 18 John F. W. Silk, Consulting Anaesthetist at King's, died. He retired from K.C.H. in 1921 (see *King's*, p. 405).

1944

During the year His Honour Hugh Sturges, K.C., resigned from the office of Vice-Chairman of the Committee of Management; he was succeeded by William Gilliatt, C.V.O. The Dean, John B. Hunter, M.C., was appointed Dean of the Faculty of Medicine of the University of London for the period 1944–6, and Frank S. Cooksey, Assistant in the Physio-therapeutic Department, was awarded the Order of the British Empire.

Mr. G. T. Whiteley, who was a member of the Committee of Management and a member of the Medical School Committee of which he had been Chairman for the period 1938–44, died in October. He gave regular and valuable service in the administration of the Medical School.

Professor Greville M. Macdonald died at Haslemere on November 3. He became the first Professor of Laryngology at King's; he was an excellent teacher and drew large classes to his lectures (see *King's*, p. 288).

William A. Brend, a distinguished former student of King's and later Lecturer in Forensic Medicine at Charing Cross Hospital Medical School, died in October (see *King's*, p. 312).

On March 24 E. C. Sarson and his wife were killed in their home during an air raid. Sarson went to King's College, London, in 1887 as an assistant in the Museum. Later he became laboratory technician in the Pathological Museum of King's College Hospital Medical School, and in April 1933 he retired on a pension from the Medical School.

1945

On June 21 Her Royal Highness the Duchess of Kent visited the Hospital and spent a considerable time in individual conversation with some of the men who had been on active service.

During the year Douglas Firth retired from King's in order to take a post at Cambridge which had been offered to him. Throughout the war period he had been in charge of the clinical teaching at the Leatherhead Emergency Hospital (see p. 105).

On January 25 Sir Herbert Smalley, M.D., aged 94, died at Hove. He had received the honour of knighthood in 1913. Herbert Smalley was a distinguished old student of King's; he joined the Medical Society of King's College, London, in 1872 (see *King's*, p. 330). He served as Medical Officer at Dartmoor, at Pentonville, and at Parkhurst; he also was Medical Inspector of Local Prisons and Superintending Officer of Convict Prisons from 1897 to 1914. He was H.M. Prison Commissioner from 1914 to 1917.

It is of particular interest to record that during recent years a King's man has been at the head of one of the great medical services of the British Empire:

The Royal Navy: Sir Arthur W. May (see *King's*, p. 154).
Sir William Henry Norman (see *King's*, p. 156).

The Army: Sir Arthur Thomas Sloggett (see *King's*, p. 160).

The Indian Medical Service: Sir Cuthbert Allan Sprawson (see *King's*, pp. 321 and 472).

The Sudan Medical Service: Edward Smyth Crispin (see *King's* p. 312).
Oliver Francis Haynes Atkey (see *King's*, p. 309).

The Prison Service: Sir Herbert Smalley (see *King's*, p. 330).

THE ROLL OF HONOUR

The names of some former students of King's who died in the service of their country during the war, 1939–45.

PRO PATRIA

Major Hugh Emrys Bonnell, R.A.M.C. *Killed by enemy action* in May 1941. He took the B.Sc. with First-Class Honours in Physics at University College, Cardiff, and came to K.C.H. Medical School in 1928. He obtained the M.R.C.S., L.R.C.P., in 1931 and at once turned to pathology; he was appointed Clinical Pathologist at the Hospital. Later he was appointed Pathologist to the East Ham Memorial Hospital and Consulting Pathologist to the Runwell Hospital.

Captain James Stephen Gregory Anthony Burns, R.A.M.C. *Killed in an ambulance smash* in 1943. He was buried with military honours in the Allied cemetery at Algiers. He qualified from King's in 1940 and joined the R.A.M.C.

Noel Clarey, R.A.M.C. *Died* in India, 1943.

John Desmond Cox, a member of the Dental School, was *posted missing*, 1944.

Surgeon-Lieut. Geoffrey S. Davis, R.N.V.R. *Reported missing, presumed killed*, 1944.

Surgeon-Lieut. Donovan James Fairweather, R.N. *Killed in action* on board H.M.S. *Southampton* in the Mediterranean, January 1941. He was educated at King's College School, King's College, London, and at K.C.H. Dental School.

Dr. Christabel Lillie Margaret Gwynne-Jones (*née* Charlesworth). *Killed by enemy action* in an air raid on Plymouth. She was the wife of Surgeon Commander T. Gwynne-Jones, R.N., who was on duty at Devonport Dockyard at the time of the raid. Christabel Gwynne-Jones qualified from King's in 1921.

Lieut. John Christopher Hawks, R.A.M.C., a battalion medical officer in the London Scottish, was *killed* during combined R.A.F. and Army Exercises on Salisbury Plain on April 19, 1941. He was educated at Epsom College, where he was head prefect, captain of Rugby football and of cricket. In 1932 he went to Magdalen College, Oxford, having obtained a classical scholarship. He entered King's College Hospital Medical School in 1937, having been awarded an Epsom College Scholarship. He was good all round at work, games, and student affairs. He was an excellent organizer and leader; he became Secretary of the Men's Common Room, 1938–9, and was captain of cricket, 1940. He had held house appointments at King's.

Surgeon-Lieut. Jack Bloor Houghton, R.N.V.R., whose name was included in an Admiralty casualty list published in March 1943, as *missing, presumed killed*. He obtained the M.R.C.S., L.R.C.P., from King's in 1940 and held a house appointment at the Leatherhead E.M.S. Hospital.

Captain Arthur Mackler, R.A.M.C., *died* during March 1943 from wounds received in the battle for the Mareth Line. Arthur Mackler, though himself wounded, continued to give directions for the dressing of his comrades and himself; he died at a casualty clearing station two days after he was injured. He obtained the M.R.C.S., L.R.C.P., from K.C.H. in 1939, and on the outbreak of war immediately volunteered for Service.

Flying Officer Harold Sidney Mellows, R.A.F.V.R. *Died* as the result of a flying accident in November 1941. He was educated at Eastbourne College, Queens' College, Cambridge, and at King's. He was a keen sportsman and was in K.C.H. Rugby fifteen. During 1935 he was Treasurer of *K.C.H. Gazette*. After being House Surgeon at King's he went into practice at West Wickham, Kent.

David Millward, R.A.M.C. *Died* while on duty at the Military Hospital, Bareilly, India, February 18, 1946.

Lieut. Roland Alexander Palmer, R.A.M.C., Parachute Field Ambulance, *lost his life* in 1943. At the United Hospital Sports in 1936 he, with others, represented King's and in the same year was chosen to represent the United Hospitals. Roland Palmer was a fine runner (see p. 165).

Jacob Phillips, R.N.V.R., was *lost at sea*.

Surgeon-Lieut. Herbert John Stammers, R.N.V.R., was reported *missing, presumed died* on the destroyer *Acasta*, June 1940. He was awarded the Jelf medal at King's College, London, in 1933 and he became qualified in 1936.

Lieut. James Pattinson Thyne, R.A.M.C. His name was included in an Army casualty list as *killed*. He was an old student of K.C.H. Medical School; he obtained the M.R.C.S., L.R.C.P., in 1928 and was House Surgeon at King's, after which he went into practice at Wandsworth.

John Keith Turner, a member of K.C.H. Dental School, was *posted missing* on air operations, March 1945.

Surgeon-Lieut. John Mortimer Watson, R.N.V.R., *lost his life* when his ship was sunk by enemy action during the Greek evacuation in April 1941. He was educated at Epsom College and Trinity Hall, Cambridge, where he was de Havilland Scholar. He entered K.C.H. Medical School in 1935 and obtained the M.R.C.S., L.R.C.P., in 1938; he was House Surgeon in 1939. He received a commission in the Navy and was posted to H.M.S. *Diamond* in 1940.

Aubrey Davis Hodges, Colonial Medical Service, died in Nigeria on May 27, 1944. He was at K.C.H. Medical School, 1933-6, and during that time he was captain of cricket and of Rugby football and was holder of the Victor Ludorum Cup (see p. 166).

ARTHUR CHARLES DOUGLAS FIRTH (1880-1948), M.A., M.D. Cantab. (1914), F.R.C.P. (1920).

Douglas Firth was educated at Harrow, Trinity College, Cambridge, and in the Medical School of St. Thomas's Hospital. He obtained the M.R.C.S., L.R.C.P., in 1907, the M.B. in 1911, and the M.R.C.P. in 1912.

After holding the appointment of Medical Registrar at the West London Hospital he was elected Assistant Physician to the Victoria Hospital for Children and to the Royal Free Hospital.

He obtained a commission as Temporary Captain in the R.A.M.C. in 1915, but was invalided out the following year.

In 1919 he was appointed Assistant Physician at King's and resigned his post at the Royal Free Hospital.

From the time of his appointment to the honorary staff at King's, Firth took a deep interest in teaching and training the students; he was also in charge of the health and medical training of the nursing staff from 1922 until he retired. In 1934 Douglas Firth, with the assistance of E. H. Green the Hospital Pharmacist, brought out a new edition of *King's College Hospital Pharmacopoeia*. During the war (1939–45) Douglas Firth was in charge of the Emergency Medical Service Hospital at Leatherhead. He was also Medical Officer to the National Provident Institution and other assurance companies. In 1938 Douglas Firth was elected a Councillor of the Royal College of Physicians, where he was Censor (1940–2) and Senior Censor in 1945.

When Firth retired from King's in 1945 he returned to Cambridge, where he accepted the post of Secretary of the Committee for Postgraduate Instruction for Demobilised Medical Officers. His wide experience as a teacher and his sympathy with students enabled him to understand the difficulties of those men whose clinical training had been interrupted by service with the Armed Forces. Soon after his return to Cambridge he was elected a Fellow of Trinity Hall. He died in January 1948. 'Kindness and loyalty to his colleagues were the hallmarks of his character.'

CHARLES WILLIAM MENELAUS HOPE (1880–1949), O.B.E. (MIL.), M.D. DUNELM (1909), F.R.C.S. (1908).

Charles Hope received his earlier education at Clifton College and at the University of Durham Medical School, where he obtained the M.B., B.S., in 1903. He then held the appointments of Senior House Surgeon, House Physician, and House Anaesthetist at the Royal Infirmary, Newcastle. Later he joined the Medical Department of King's College, London, and at the same time became Clinical Assistant in the Throat Department at St. Mary's Hospital.

From 1909 to 1914 he was Assistant Surgeon at the Golden Square Throat and Ear Hospital. In 1910 he was appointed Clinical Assistant to Sir St. Clair Thomson at King's College Hospital, and he continued to work in the Throat Department until 1914, when he was elected Assistant Surgeon in the Department, becoming Surgeon in 1922 and Consulting Surgeon in 1940.

He was also Consulting Surgeon to the Ear, Nose, and Throat Department of the Finchley Memorial Hospital, and Consulting Laryngologist to the Royal Eye Hospital, London.

During the war (1914–18) Charles Hope was Major, R.A.M.C., at St. John Ambulance Brigade Hospital, Étaples.

In 1923 he became Honorary Secretary of King's College Hospital Clubs' and Societies' Union and in 1926 he was elected President, an office which he filled for fourteen years. Throughout the whole time he was President he took the greatest interest in its welfare.

Hope was the author of *Suppuration in the Nasal Sinuses* and *A Method of Eneucleation of the Tonsils.*

Charles Hope, officer of the Order of St. John of Jerusalem, died on April 21, 1949.

PROFESSOR EDWARD MAPOTHER (1881–1940), M.D. Lond. (1908), F.R.C.P. (1927), F.R.C.S. (1910).

Edward Mapother was born in Merrion Square, Dublin. He was the son of Edward Dillon Mapother, a distinguished anatomist who became President of the Royal College of Surgeons of Ireland.

Mapother was educated at University College School, University College, and at University College Hospital, where he was House Physician to Risien Russell. He obtained the M.B., B.S., in 1905 and the M.R.C.P. in 1920. He was elected a Fellow of University College in 1937.

At the outbreak of war in 1914 Mapother joined the R.A.M.C. and saw service in France, in Mesopotamia, and in India. In 1917 he became the O.C. the Neurological Section of the 2nd Western General Hospital and remained in command until he returned to London in 1919, when he was appointed Medical Superintendent of the Ministry of Pensions Hospital for War Neuroses established at the Maudsley Hospital. When the Maudsley was opened in 1923 as a centre for treatment, research, and teaching, Mapother was selected to be the Medical Superintendent. He so moulded and directed that institution that it became the acknowledged centre of teaching and research in Psychiatry in England. In 1937 he was appointed to the newly created chair of Clinical Psychiatry in the University of London. This was an obvious tribute to the great impetus which he had given to psychiatric research through the school, which he had built up at the Maudsley. He resigned his post at the Maudsley in 1939.

Mapother was the Chief Consultant to the Ex-Service Welfare Society and Consulting Psychiatrist to the Maida Vale Hospital for Nervous Diseases and to the Queen Alexandra Military Hospital, Millbank.

At the Royal College of Physicians he was a member of the Council (1937–8), and in 1936 he was a Bradshaw Lecturer.

At King's he was appointed Lecturer in Psychological Medicine in 1922, becoming Physician for Psychological Medicine in 1923. He was President of the Listerian Society (1936–7).

Edward Mapother died on March 20, 1940, after a long illness, and his death removed an outstanding figure from English Psychiatry. He believed that psychological medicine was best advanced by the use

I

of scientific methods and by adherence to the principles of clinical medicine, and he would have no one on his staff at the Maudsley who had not had previously some practical experience in general medicine.

He wrote 'The Schizophrenic Paranoid Series' (*Lancet*), vol. 1; *A Plea of Nominalism in Psychiatry*; and *Mental Symptoms associated with Head Injury*.

TERENCE EDWARD CAWTHORNE, F.R.C.S. (1930).

Terence Cawthorne obtained the M.R.C.S., L.R.C.P., in 1924 and was then appointed House Surgeon in the Ear, Nose, and Throat Department at King's. In 1928 he was appointed Registrar in that department, and when the Oto-Rhinological and the Rhino-Laryngological Departments were amalgamated in 1932 he was appointed Junior Surgeon to the department, becoming Surgeon in 1939.

Classical music has been Terence Cawthorne's hobby for many years, and he has frequently given gramophone record recitals with appropriate running commentaries to the students and to the nurses at King's. In 1939 he was Deputy Chief Medical Officer of Sector IX, E.M.S., and was Dean of the Medical School from October 1946 to the end of January 1948.

Terence Cawthorne's chief medical interest is that of Otology; he has written articles on 'The Human Vestibular Function', 'Vestibular Injuries', and on 'Ménière's Disease'. He is Aural Surgeon at the National Hospital, Queen Square, and Consulting Adviser to the Ministry of Health in Oto-laryngology. He is an Honorary Fellow of the American Laryngological, Rhinological, and Otological Society and an Honorary Member of the American Otological Society. He was elected Hunterian Professor at the Royal College of Surgeons for 1949.

MACDONALD CRITCHLEY, M.D. Bristol (1924), F.R.C.P. (1930).

Macdonald Critchley was a distinguished student at the University of Bristol, where he was awarded the Lady Haberfield Scholarship in Medicine and the Markham Skerritt Prize for Original Research. He obtained the M.R.C.S., L.R.C.P., in 1922, after which he held the following appointments: House Physician at Great Ormond Street Hospital for Sick Children, Resident Medical Officer at the Hospital for Epilepsy and Paralysis, Maida Vale, and Resident Medical Officer and Registrar at the National Hospital, Queen Square, where he is now Physician and Dean.

At the Royal College of Physicians he was Goulstonian Lecturer (the Neurology of Old Age) in 1931, Bradshaw Lecturer in 1942, and Croonian Lecturer in 1945. At the Royal College of Surgeons he was Hunterian Professor, 1934–5, and at the University of Bristol he was Long Fox Lecturer in 1935.

During the First World War (1914–18) Macdonald Critchley served during 1917–18, and throughout the Second World War (1939–45) he was Temporary Surgeon-Captain, R.N.V.R., and Consulting Neurologist to the Royal Navy.

When Aldren Turner retired from King's in 1928, Kinnier Wilson became head of the Neurological Department and Macdonald Critchley was appointed Junior Neurologist, becoming Physician for Nervous Diseases in 1935. After the death of Kinnier Wilson in 1937, Critchley became head of the Department of Neurology.

During the session 1934–5 Macdonald Critchley was President of the Listerian Society. He has written numerous articles on nervous diseases, including a biographical appreciation of Sir William Gowers (1845–1915).

WILLIAM INGLEDEW DAGGETT (b. 1900), M.A., M.B., B.Ch. Cantab. (1925), F.R.C.S. (1926).

William Daggett was an Exhibitioner at Sedbergh and a Scholar of Caius College, Cambridge, where he was awarded First Class Honours in the Natural Sciences Tripos. He came to K.C.H. Medical School in 1922 when he was awarded a Burney Yeo Scholarship. He was a member of the Cricket First Eleven and became Captain. He obtained the M.R.C.S., L.R.C.P., in 1924 and was successively Assistant Casualty Officer, House Surgeon, House Surgeon to the special departments, and Sambrooke Surgical Registrar. In 1927 he was appointed Registrar to the Ear, Nose, and Throat Department, in 1928 he became Junior Aural Surgeon, and in 1935 Aural Surgeon. In 1931 William Daggett undertook the Treasurership of the Clubs' and Societies' Union.

He became Surgeon-in-charge of the Ear, Nose, and Throat Department at King's and Consulting Ear, Nose, and Throat Surgeon at the Maudsley Hospital.

During the war (1939–45) he joined the R.A.M.C. as an Ear, Nose, and Throat Specialist. He served in Malta, Egypt, and in India. He became Brigadier Consultant to G.H.Q., India, and South East Asia Command, and in 1945 was appointed Brigadier Consultant to the Army.

William Daggett has written important articles on Aural Surgery.

HAROLD CLIFFORD EDWARDS (b. 1899), C.B.E., M.S. (1928), F.R.C.S. (1926).

Harold Edwards came to King's from University College, Cardiff, and during his student days he was a member of the Rugby Fifteen. He obtained the M.B., B.S., in 1923 and was appointed House Surgeon. In 1924 he became Sambrooke Surgical Registrar, later Senior Surgical Registrar, and in 1927 Senior Surgical Tutor. He was appointed Assistant Surgeon in 1928 and Surgeon in 1934. He was awarded the Robert Jones Gold Medal and Prize by the British Orthopaedic Association in 1930. At the Royal College of Surgeons he was Jacksonian Prizeman in 1932 and Hunterian Professor in 1934.

From 1941 to 1946 Harold Edwards was on war service in the R.A.M.C. and became Brigadier, Consulting Surgeon to the Southern Command and later to the Central Mediterranean Forces.

Harold Edwards became a member of the Court of Examiners at the Royal College of Surgeons. In 1948 he succeeded Terence E. Cawthorne as Dean of the Medical School.

He has published *Surgical Emergencies in Children, Diverticula and Diverticulitis of the Intestine, The Value of Gastroscopy,* and *Recent Advances in Surgery.*

SIR (HAROLD ARTHUR) THOMAS FAIRBANK (b. 1876), D.S.O., O.B.E., M.B. Lond. (1898), M.S. (1903), F.R.C.S. (1901), Hon. M.Ch. in Orthopaedics of Liverpool University (1939), L.D.S. (1899).

Thomas Fairbank was educated at Epsom College and at Charing Cross Hospital Medical School, where he was awarded an open Entrance Scholarship. It was originally intended that he should join his two uncles, one of whom was an 'old King's man', in dental practice, but although qualified in dentistry he never practised. After being House Surgeon at Charing Cross Hospital Fairbank served as a Civil Surgeon in the Boer War (1899–1901). In South Africa he met and sometimes assisted Sir Watson Cheyne, who was away from 'King's' serving as Consulting Surgeon to the Army. On returning to England towards the end of 1900, Fairbank was appointed Resident Superintendent at the Hospital for Sick Children, Great Ormond Street, with which hospital he was actively associated for twenty-eight years and of which he became Consulting Surgeon. After holding the post of Surgical Registrar he was appointed Orthopaedic Surgeon to Charing Cross Hospital, the first hospital in London to elect a surgeon to its staff for orthopaedic work only. He was also appointed Surgeon to the Miller General Hospital.

Being an officer in a Territorial Field Ambulance, he became mobilized at the outbreak of the war (1914–18) and served abroad, in Flanders and Salonika, for four years, the latter part of the period he spent as Consulting Surgeon. When holding the latter post he was under the command of, and in touch with, Sir Maurice P. C. Holt, K.C.B., a distinguished old King's man (see *King's*, p. 224), who was Director of Medical Services in the Army in Salonika.

In 1919 Fairbank was invited to take charge of the newly formed Orthopaedic Department at King's; this he did with the assistance of Jennings Marshall, M.D., M.S., F.R.C.S., who was appointed Assistant Orthopaedic Surgeon. In 1922 with the help of St. J. Dudley Buxton, M.B., B.S., F.R.C.S., who had succeeded Jennings Marshall as Assistant Orthopaedic Surgeon, Fairbank started a special Fracture Clinic to which all ambulatory fracture cases were to be referred by the casualty officers either for approval, criticism, or for treatment. This was the first fracture clinic started in a hospital in London and one of the first in this country.

On retiring from the active staff in 1936 Fairbank was appointed Consulting Orthopaedic Surgeon to the Hospital and Emeritus Lecturer in Orthopaedic Surgery in the Medical School.

He is Consulting Orthopaedic Surgeon to the Lord Mayor Treloar Cripples' Hospital, Alton, and to the Queen Alexandra Military Hospital, Millbank. In 1926–7 Fairbank was President of the British Orthopaedic Association.

With the late Sir Robert Jones, Fairbank held the first examination for the M.Ch. (Orth.) degree at the Liverpool University, and in 1929 he delivered the Lady Jones Lecture at that university. In 1938 he was appointed, by the Royal College of Surgeons, the first 'Robert Jones Lecturer'. He was Consulting Adviser in Orthopaedics in the E.M.S. (1939–45) and he is Honorary Consultant in Orthopaedics to the Army. He was knighted in 1946. Sir Thomas Fairbank has written extensively on orthopaedic subjects, one of his latest articles being on 'Increased and Decreased Density of Bone with Special Reference to Fibrosis of Marrow' in the *British Journal of Surgery*.

VERNON FREDERICK HALL, M.R.C.S., L.R.C.P. (1927), D.A. (1939), F.F.A., R.C.S.

Vernon Hall joined the Medical School of King's in 1922 and immediately took a practical interest in the games. In 1924 he was a member of the team which won the Junior Inter-Hospitals Cricket Cup, and from 1926 to 1931 he was a member of the Rugby Fifteen.

In 1927 he was appointed Assistant Casualty Officer at King's, later House Surgeon, then Resident Anaesthetist. At one period he was House Surgeon at All Saints' Hospital. He was appointed Honorary Assistant Anaesthetist at King's in 1931.

Vernon Hall joined the R.A.M.C. in 1942 and remained on duty until 1946. During most of the time he was in India and held the following appointments: Command Anaesthetist to the Ceylon Army; Adviser in Anaesthetics, Eastern Command; Adviser in Anaesthetics, Allied Land Forces, S.E. Asia; and lastly Brigadier Consulting Anaesthetist, Indian Command.

In 1946 Vernon Hall was appointed Vice-Dean of the Medical School. In 1948 he became appointed a member of the first Board of the newly constituted Faculty of Anaesthetists of the Royal College of Surgeons and received the Fellowship of the Faculty.

Besides being Senior Anaesthetist at King's, Vernon Hall is Anaesthetist at the Evelina Hospital for Children and at the National Hospital for Nervous Diseases, Queen Square.

He has written articles on Anaesthesia.

JOHN BOWMAN HUNTER (b. 1890), C.B.E., M.C., M.B.,
    M.Ch. Cantab. (1921), F.R.C.S. (1921).

John Hunter was educated at Bedford School and at St. John's College, Cambridge, where he was awarded First Class Honours in the Natural Sciences Tripos in 1912. He entered the Medical School of University College, London, where he became Liston Silver and Gold Medallist. He obtained the M.R.C.S., L.R.C.P., in 1914 and during the war (1914–18) he went to France as Lieutenant in Queen Victoria's Rifles. In 1915 he was transferred to the R.A.M.C., became Captain, and was awarded the M.C. in 1916. Later he became stationed in Northern Russia after the Armistice until June 1919. He then returned to University College Hospital, where he was appointed House Physician to Sir John Rose Bradford, and later House Surgeon to Wilfred Trotter. He then became Surgical Registrar and Assistant to the Surgical Unit at University College Hospital. In 1925 he was appointed Assistant Surgeon at the Royal Northern Hospital and Surgeon at the Royal Chest Hospital. In 1927 John Hunter was appointed Assistant Surgeon at King's and in 1938 he became Dean of the Medical School, an office which he held until 1946. During 1938–9 he was President of the Golf Club and of the Sailing Club at King's.

In 1939 John B. Hunter was appointed Group Officer in the Emergency Medical Service and remained in office until the end of the war in 1945.

He was Dean of the Faculty of Medicine, University of London, for the periods 1944–6 and 1946–8.

WILFRID PERCY HENRY SHELDON (b. 1901), M.D. LOND. (1925), F.R.C.P. (1933).

Wilfrid Sheldon was educated in King's College Hospital Medical School, where he was awarded a Medical Entrance Exhibition in 1918, the Rabbeth Scholarship in 1919, the Alfred Hughes Anatomy Prize in 1921, and the Tanner Prize in 1923; he also became Senior Scholar and obtained the M.R.C.S., L.R.C.P., in 1923. At the M.B., B.S. examination in 1924 he was awarded honours in Medicine. At the Hospital for Sick Children, Great Ormond Street, he became Medical Registrar and Pathologist; later he was elected Physician. In 1928 Wilfrid Sheldon was appointed Assistant Physician to the Children's Department at King's, and from that date he was associated with Sir Frederic Still until 1933, when the latter retired from King's; then Wilfrid Sheldon became Physician-in-charge of the department. In 1939 Philip Rainsford Evans, M.D. Manchester, M.R.C.P., was appointed Assistant Physician to the Children's Department. Shortly after war broke out in 1939, Wilfrid Sheldon and Philip Evans organized a children's hospital at Cuckfield for the 60,000 children who had been evacuated from London. In 1943 the Cuckfield Hospital was taken over by the Canadians and Philip Evans joined the Army, becoming Lieut.-Colonel, R.A.M.C.

Wilfrid Sheldon then organized another children's hospital at Haywards Heath. In 1946 Philip Evans returned to King's, but in a short time he was offered, and accepted, the post of Director of the Children's Department at Guy's Hospital, so that he resigned his appointment at King's. In July 1948 Mary Wilmers, Registrar to the Children's Department at King's, who had done excellent work throughout the war during the air raids on London, while she was stationed at K.C.H., was appointed Assistant Physician to help Wilfrid Sheldon in the work of the Children's Department.

During the session 1938–9 Wilfrid Sheldon was President of the Listerian Society.

He is the author of *Diseases of Infancy and Children*, *Amyoplasia Congenita*, and *Spectrographic Analysis of Human Tissues*.

MATTHEW SYDNEY THOMSON (b. 1894), M.A., M.D. CANTAB. (1922), F.R.C.P. (1933), F.R.S. EDIN. (1931).

Sydney Thomson was educated at Merchant Taylors' School and became a Foundation Scholar of Downing College, Cambridge. He was awarded a Burney Yeo Scholarship at King's in 1917. In 1918 he obtained the M.R.C.S., L.R.C.P., and was appointed Clinical Assistant in the Dermatological Department and worked under the direction of Professor Arthur Whitfield. When the Department for Venereal Diseases was reorganized in 1919 Sydney Thomson was appointed to assist in that department. In 1927 he was elected Junior Physician for Diseases of the Skin and promoted Physician in 1934. He is also Physician for Diseases of the Skin at the Belgrave Hospital for Children. During the war (1939–45) Sydney Thomson went into residence at K.C.H. and was in charge of the casualty work as well as the skin work of Sector IX. He was President of the Section of Dermatology of the Royal Society of Medicine, 1945–7, and President of the British Association of Dermatology in 1948. He is an Honorary Member of the Dermatological Society of Holland and corresponding member of the Dermatological Society of Hungary and of the Danish Dermatological Society.

He is the author of *Tumours of the Skin, Investigation into the Causation of Pityriasis Rosea*, and of *Poikilodermia Congenitale*.

SURGEON REAR-ADMIRAL SIR CECIL PEMBREY GREY WAKELEY (b. 1892), K.B.E. (Mil.) (1946), C.B. (Mil.) (1941), F.R.C.S. (1921), F.R.S. Edin. (1926), D.Sc. Lond. (1932), F.K.C. (1933).

Cecil Wakeley was educated at Dulwich College and King's College Hospital Medical School; he obtained the M.R.C.S., L.R.C.P., in 1915, having previously been Assistant Demonstrator of Anatomy at King's College. He was House Surgeon to Boyce Barrow who had returned to King's to assist in the surgical work of the Hospital during the war (1914–18). In 1915 Cecil Wakeley joined the Royal Navy, but in 1919 he returned to King's and was appointed Senior Surgical Registrar and Surgical Tutor; he became Junior Surgeon in 1922 and Surgeon in 1929. On the retirement of Arthur Edmunds, Cecil Wakeley was appointed Consulting Surgeon to the Royal Navy. During the session 1924–5 he was President of the Listerian Society. From 1939 to 1946 he was Surgeon Rear-Admiral in the Navy At the Royal College of Surgeons Cecil Wakeley was Arris and Gale Lecturer in 1924, Hunterian Professor in 1928, Arnott Demonstrator in 1933, and Bradshaw Lecturer in 1947. In 1936 he was elected a member of the Council of the Royal College of Surgeons and was a member of the Court of Examiners from 1933 to 1943. He has been a member of the General Medical Council since 1943.

In 1949 Cecil Wakeley was elected President of the Royal College of Surgeons of England.

Cecil Wakeley has been Editor of the *Medical Press* since 1930, Editorial Secretary to the *British Journal of Surgery* since 1939, and Editor of the *Annals of the Royal College of Surgeons* since 1947.

He is the author of *Student's Handbook of Surgical Operations* and *Textbook of Neuro-Radiology*.

SOME 'OLD KING'S STUDENTS' ON DUTY DURING 1939–45.

GEOFFREY THOMAS WILLOUGHBY CASHELL (b. 1905), M.B., B.S. Lond. (1933), F.R.C.S. Edin. (1933), A.K.C.

Geoffrey Cashell received his earlier education at Westminster School. He entered the Science Department of King's College, London, in 1924, but later transferred to the Medical Faculty.

While at the College he was Secretary of King's College Medical Society. He came to the Hospital Medical School in 1928 and in 1929 was Secretary of the Listerian Society. He also took a prominent part in the 'Christmas shows'.

He obtained the M.R.C.S., L.R.C.P., in 1930 and was appointed Ophthalmic House Surgeon, later Urological House Surgeon at King's. He also worked at the Royal London Ophthalmic Hospital, Moorfields, and at the Royal Westminster Ophthalmic Hospital.

He was appointed Honorary Ophthalmic Surgeon at the Royal Berkshire Hospital in 1933.

During the war (1939–45) Geoffrey Cashell was a Wing-Commander, R.A.F.V.R., and adviser in Ophthalmology in the R.A.F. in South East Asia.

He has written on 'Treatment of Concomitant and Latent Strabismus', on 'The Causes and Treatment of Epiphora', and other ophthalmic subjects.

LEONARD DUNCAN ALBERT HUSSEY (b. 1891), O.B.E., B.Sc. Lond., M.R.C.S., L.R.C.P. (1923), A.K.C. (1913).

Leonard Hussey became a student at King's College, London, in 1909. He passed the B.Sc. with honours in 1913. During the time he was at King's College he was a member of the Infantry Unit of the University of London O.T.C. and in 1912 he received a commission in the same company.

He was Anthropologist to the Wellcome Sudan Expedition from 1913 to 1914, and from 1914 to 1916 he was Meteorologist to Sir

Ernest Shackleton's Antarctic Expedition in the *Endurance* which sailed in August 1914.

After reaching South Georgia, the *Endurance* left for the south. After Bruces' Coats Land was passed and Caird Coast discovered the ship was beset in heavy pack ice. 'After drifting for nine months she was crushed in the ice on the 27th October 1915 about 200 miles from the nearest land and 1,000 miles from human help.' The party proceeded by sledge and boats to Elephant Island, which was reached on April 15, 1916, and lived under two old boats until rescued on August 30, 1916.

'Realizing that no search expedition would be likely to visit Elephant Island, Shackleton determined to reach South Georgia in an effort to bring help. With five companions he made a voyage of 800 miles in a twenty-two foot boat through some of the stormiest seas in the world, crossed the unknown lofty interior of South Georgia, and reached a Norwegian whaling station on the north coast. After three attempts in different vessels, Shackleton succeeded (August 30, 1916) in rescuing the rest of the *Endurance* party (one of which was Hussey) and bringing them to South America.' (*Dictionary of National Biography*.)

After his return to England, Hussey transferred to the Royal Garrison Artillery and went to France in 1917, where he served for some months. From 1918 to 1919 he was with Shackleton in the North Russian Expeditionary Force.

As Captain in the R.G.A., Hussey was demobilized in 1919 and returned to the Medical Faculty of King's College, London.

He joined K.C.H. Medical School in 1920 but returned to the Antarctic with Sir Ernest Shackleton's Expedition in the R.S.Y. *Quest* which sailed in September 1921.

During the expedition Sir Ernest Henry Shackleton (1874–1922), C.V.O., O.B.E., one of the greatest explorers that the world has ever known, died suddenly on January 4, and was buried by his friend and companion, Leonard Hussey, at the Whaling Station, Grytviken, on the lonely island of South Georgia on the edge of the Antarctic ice.

When the expedition returned, Hussey came back to King's. On May 30, 1922, an informal musical evening by the Hospital Musical Society was given to welcome him back from the Shackleton–Rowett Expedition. The chair was taken by Viscount Hambleden, who made a speech of welcome in which he expressed his admiration for men who, like Hussey, encountered many dangers and suffered innumerable hardships for the furtherance of science and discovery.

Hussey is an artist with the banjo, and has delighted audiences in the Sudan, in the Antarctic, and at K.C.H. Musical Society with his banjo solos.

He obtained the M.R.C.S., L.R.C.P., in 1923 and was appointed Second Casualty Officer. After leaving King's he became House Physician at the Belgrave Hospital for Children, to which hospital he afterwards became Anaesthetist.

In September 1930 a bed was endowed at K.C.H. in memory of Sir Ernest Shackleton, over which is the following inscription:

> 'Shackleton Bed.
>
> In memory of Sir Ernest Shackleton,
> Antarctic Explorer.
>
> Endowed by one of his comrades, who
> was a student of this Hospital and
> an old Strandian, and by Strand School.'

In October 1931 Hussey gave a lecture before the Listerian Society in which he told the story of Sir Ernest Shackleton's Expedition to the Antarctic in 1914. It was a fascinating lecture, illustrated by more than one hundred magnificent slides, all of which were taken in the Antarctic. During the war (1939–45) Leonard Hussey was a Squadron Leader, R.A.F.

He is the co-author of 'Scurvy in its Relation to Polar Expeditions' (*Lancet*, 1921).

GEOFFREY LAWRENCE SAMUEL KONSTAM, M.D. LOND. (1928), F.R.C.P. (1939).

Geoffrey Konstam was educated at Westminster School (1913–18). During 1918 he did war service with the Royal Engineers, and in 1919 he joined the Medical Faculty of King's College, London. During 1919 to 1921 he was Secretary and later Captain of the King's College Lawn Tennis Club. In 1921 he came to K.C.H. and obtained the M.R.C.S., L.R.C.P., in 1923, when he was appointed House Surgeon. After holding resident appointments at other hospitals in London, he passed the M.B., B.S., in 1926 and in 1927 he was appointed First Assistant and Medical Registrar at the London Hospital.

During the time that Geoffrey Konstam was at King's he was Captain of the Lawn Tennis Club (see *King's*, p. 479).

In 1932 he was appointed Assistant Physician to the West London Hospital and in 1937 he was promoted Physician and Physician with charge of the Cardiographic Department.

During the war (1939–45) Geoffrey Konstam was Lieut.-Col.,

R.A.M.C. (1940–5) and officer-in-charge of the Medical Divisions of the 43rd and 63rd General Hospitals.

He has published *Syphilis of the Lung with Pulmonary Arteritis* (Ayerza's Disease) and other cardiovascular disturbances.

ISABELLA LOUISE HAMILTON LIVINGSTONE, M.D. LOND. (1929), M.R.C.P. (1930).

Louise Livingstone was educated at St. Winifred's, Eastbourne, and at the Royal School of Medicine for Women. She came to King's in 1924, obtained the M.R.C.S., L.R.C.P., in 1926, the M.B., B.S., in 1927, and held the appointments of Assistant Casualty Officer, House Surgeon, and Obstetric and Gynaecological House Surgeon.

On leaving King's in 1928 she went to the Royal Northern Hospital, where she was successively Obstetric House Surgeon, House Physician, and Casualty Officer. During the latter half of 1930 she was Senior Resident Medical Officer at the Queen's Hospital for Children.

She has held the post of Honorary Secretary to the University of London Medical Graduates Society.

During the war (1939–45) she was a Major, I.M.S.

DAVID JAMES MACMYN, T.D., M.A., M.B., B.CH. CANTAB. (1928).

David MacMyn was at Fettes College from 1916 to 1921, when he left with an Open Classical Exhibition to Pembroke College, Cambridge. He came to King's in 1925, having been awarded a Burney Yeo Scholarship. He obtained the M.R.C.S., L.R.C.P., in 1927 and was appointed House Surgeon to the Hampstead General Hospital. He returned to King's and was successively House Physician, House Surgeon, Senior Casualty Officer, and during 1930–2 he was Sambrooke Surgical Registrar. In 1932 he was awarded a Rockefeller Travelling Fellowship when he worked at the Mayo Clinic as First Surgical Assistant in the Neuro-Surgical Section.

David MacMyn was a member of the Cambridge University Rugby Fifteen, 1921–4 inclusive. He played for King's and in 1929–30 he was captain of the team. During 1928–30 he played for the United Hospitals. He also played for the London Scottish, Middlesex, the Barbarians, and for Scotland. Between 1925 and 1929 he was in the Scottish Fifteen on eleven occasions. In 1927 he was Captain of the British Rugby Football Team which toured the Argentine and which won all its matches without a try being scored against them (see *King's*, p. 475).

MacMyn is a Major in the R.A.M.C., T.A., attached to the London Scottish; during the war (1939–45) he was a Colonel, R.A.M.C.

He is the author of *Carbuncle of the Kidney*, and *Neuro-Surgery in the Treatment of Diseases of Peripheral Blood Vessels*.

SYDNEY SMITH (b. 1887), M.B., B.S. LOND. (1914), F.R.C.P. (1936), BRIGADIER, R.A.M.C.

Sidney Smith was educated at King's College School and in the Medical Department of King's College, London. He was awarded the Tanner Prize and in 1912 he obtained special medicine and surgery prizes. He was Secretary of King's College Hospital Medical Society for the session 1911–12. He obtained the M.R.C.S., L.R.C.P., in 1912 and was appointed Ophthalmic House Surgeon and Ophthalmic Clinical Assistant in the Out-patient Department.

After leaving King's he joined the R.A.M.C., and in 1926 he obtained the M.R.C.P.

At one time he was Surgeon to Dr. Clemow's Hospital for wounded Turks at Constantinople and Assistant Professor of Tropical Medicine at the R.A.M. College and was Honorary Physician to H.M. the King, 1941–4.

In 1942 Sidney Smith was Consultant for Tropical Diseases at the General Headquarters of the Middle East Force; he was later Consulting Physician to the Southern and Eastern Commands, and Consulting Physician to the Royal Army Military College, Millbank.

He is the author of 'Surgical Experiences during the Balkan War', *Lancet*, 1913, and 'Notes on the Treatment of Hernia Cerebri', *B.M.J.*, 1916.

KING'S COLLEGE HOSPITAL AND THE MEDICAL SCHOOL DURING THE IMMEDIATE POST-WAR PERIOD
1945 and 1946

1945

ON July 29 W. Aldren Turner, C.B., Consulting Physician at King's, died in Edinburgh. He first came to King's in 1892 in order to assist Professor David Ferrier in the newly established neuro-pathological laboratory at King's College; Aldren Turner became appointed on the honorary staff of the Hospital in 1899, and he retired from active duties at King's in 1928 (see *King's*, p. 414). From 1919 to 1940 he was Neurologist to the War Office Medical Board and from 1930 to 1943 he was consultant adviser to the Ministry of Pensions.

On November 29 Arthur Edmunds, C.B., Consulting Surgeon to King's, died in the Hospital. He joined the Medical Department of King's College in 1896 and, until he retired from the active staff of the Hospital in 1934, he worked hard in the interest of the Hospital and Medical School. During the war (1939–45) he, at the age of 66, returned to surgery at Cuckfield E.M.S. Hospital in Sussex (see p. 104 and *King's*, p. 396).

At the end of the year J. Myles Bickerton, Ophthalmic Surgeon, resigned his appointment. He was appointed Assistant Ophthalmic Surgeon in 1928 and Ophthalmic Surgeon in 1931.

After seven years as Assistant Ophthalmic Surgeon Keith Lyle was promoted Ophthalmic Surgeon.

1946

In the New Year's Honours List, John B. Hunter, M.C., the Dean, was awarded the C.B.E. (Civil Division) in recognition of his work as Sector Hospital Officer, and H. A. Thomas Fairbank, D.S.O., O.B.E., received the accolade of Knight Bachelor.

In the Birthday Honours List, Surgeon Rear-Admiral Cecil P. G. Wakeley, C.B., Senior Surgeon at King's and one of the Vice-Presidents of the Royal College of Surgeons, was awarded the

K.B.E., and during the year Harold C. Edwards was awarded the C.B.E.

In October John B. Hunter retired from the office of Dean of the Medical School to which he had been appointed in 1938. During the period in which he was Dean he was assisted by A. Wallis Kendall, the Vice-Dean, and during the time that Wallis Kendall was on service duty John Hunter was assisted by Terence Cawthorne, who from 1939 to 1946 was acting Vice-Dean. John B. Hunter was succeeded in office by Terence E. Cawthorne and Vernon F. Hall was appointed Vice-Dean.

The Hospital and Medical School owe John Hunter a deep debt of gratitude for his strenuous and devoted service throughout the period that he was Dean.

During the year William Gilliatt was elected President of the Royal College of Obstetricians and Gynaecologists (see *King's*, p. 311), and R. D. Lawrence was awarded 'The Banting Medal of the American Diabetes Association' for 'distinguished service in the interest of doctor and patient' (see p. 81).

During 1946 the Departments of Morbid Anatomy and Biochemistry were considerably expanded and reorganized. In July Henry A. Magnus, M.D. Lond., of St. Bartholomew's Hospital was appointed Morbid Anatomist and Sheila M. Newstead, M.B., B.S. Lond., M.R.C.P., became Assistant Clinical Pathologist.

During the year the Medical Research Council established their Dental Research Unit in the Medical School under the Directorship of J. J. D. King, Ph.D., L.D.S., R.C.S., who was then appointed Assistant Dental Surgeon to the Hospital.

The Senior Anaesthetist at King's, Hugh A. Richards, resigned; he was appointed Consulting Anaesthetist to the Hospital, and Philip R. Evans, Assistant Physician in the Department for Diseases of Children, also resigned his appointment at King's, upon his election as Children's Physician and Director of the Department of Child Health at Guy's Hospital.

In order that the Hospital might retain the services of some of the senior members of the honorary medical staff who were due to retire on account of the age-limit of 60 years, it was agreed that the appointments should be extended until the members reach the age of 65. The members of the honorary medical staff so retained constitute the active consulting staff, and are entitled to have the care of in-patients and to see out-patients; they are required to assist in teaching. In November 1946 the following were appointed members of the honorary active consulting staff:

William Gilliatt, c.v.o., m.d., m.s., f.r.c.s., p.r.c.o.g. } *Obstetric and Gynae-*
Alexander C. Palmer, o.b.e., m.b., b.s., f.r.c.s.   } *cological Surgeons.*
John Everidge, o.b.e., f.r.c.s.: *Urological Surgeon.*
Victor E. Negus, m.s., f.r.c.s.: *Surgeon for Diseases of the Ear, Nose, and Throat.*

Towards the end of December E. Bellis Clayton, Director of the Physical Treatment Department, resigned his appointment; he was given the title of Consulting Physician to that department (see p. 66). He was succeeded by Frank S. Cooksey, O.B.E., M.D. Lond., D.Phys.M., who was appointed Director of the Physical Treatment Department in January 1947.

On December 31 Miss L. Stock, the Accountant, retired after nearly twenty-eight years of devoted service to the Medical School.

On January 8 Hugh A. B. Whitelocke died. He was Senior Honorary Surgeon at the Radcliffe Infirmary and a Colonel, R.A.M.C. (Reserve), T.D. (see *King's*, p. 347).

On March 3 William Henry Dobie, M.B., C.M. Edin., died at Chester in his 90th year. He and James Altham came from Edinburgh in 1877 so as to act as Professor Joseph Lister's first surgical dressers at King's (see *King's*, p. 167).

On July 22 Hector Alfred Colwell died after a long illness at the age of 71. He became Assistant Radiologist at King's in 1921 and in 1925 he was appointed Director of Radio-therapeutics in succession to Robert Knox (see *King's* p. 401). Colwell retired from King's in 1936 (see *King's* p. 357).

JOHN EVERIDGE, O.B.E. (Mil.), F.R.C.S. (1912).

John Everidge was educated at King's College School and in the Medical Faculty of King's College, London, where he became Alfred Hughes Anatomy Prizeman, Junior Scholar in 1904, and Senior Scholar in 1907. He obtained the M.R.C.S., L.R.C.P., in 1908 and was appointed House Surgeon. In 1912 he became Sambrooke Surgical Registrar and Surgical Tutor. During the war (1914–18) he was Surgical Specialist to the Forces in France with the rank of Major, R.A.M.C. (T). In 1919 John Everidge was appointed Junior Urologist and Junior Surgeon at King's and he became Senior Urologist and Lecturer on Urology when Sir John Thomson-Walker retired in 1929 (see *King's*, p. 411).

After the war (1939–45) when duties at the Hospital and Medical School were rearranged he became appointed Active Consulting Urological Surgeon. He was President of the Listerian Society 1922–3.

In his student days John Everidge was a keen lawn-tennis player; he was a member of the Lawn Tennis Six in 1906; the other members of the team being Harold W. Wiltshire, E. W. Matthews, A. Scott Gillett, Douglas Hamilton, and R. B. Roe. Later, when a member of the Hospital staff, John Everidge played for the staff in the matches 'Students *v.* Staff' (see *King's*, pp. 477, 478).

He has written articles on Urinary Surgery and is Chairman of the Editorial Committee of the *British Journal of Urology*.

SIR WILLIAM GILLIATT (b. 1884), K.C.V.O. (1949), M.D. Lond., Gold Medallist (1910), M.S. (1912), F.R.C.P. (1947), F.R.C.S. (1912), F.R.C.O.G. (1929).

William Gilliatt received his medical education at the Middlesex Hospital Medical School, where he was a Scholar and Gold Medallist, also Obstetric and Gynaecological Registrar and Tutor. He was appointed Assistant Obstetric and Gynaecological Surgeon at King's and Lecturer on Gynaecology in the Medical School in 1916. On the resignation of Hugh Playfair in 1925 William Gilliatt became Senior Obstetric and Gynaecological Surgeon, a post which he held until 1946, when he became a member of the active consulting staff. He is Consulting Surgeon to the Samaritan Free Hospital for Women. During the War (1914–18) he served as Captain, R.A.M.C. In 1946 William Gilliatt followed Sir Eardley Lancelot Holland (see *King's*, p. 340) as President of the Royal College of Obstetricians and Gynaecologists; previously he was a member of the Council, also Honorary Treasurer. He has been a member of the Committee of Management of King's College Hospital since 1932, and in 1945 he was appointed Vice-Chairman; during the illness of Viscount Hambleden, William Gilliatt occupied the chair. In 1948 he received a knighthood and became appointed Gynaecologist to H.R.H. Princess Elizabeth.

VICTOR EWINGS NEGUS (b. 1887), D.Sc. Manch. (1950), M.S. Lond., F.R.C.S. (1921), F.K.C. (1945).

Victor Negus was educated at King's College School, which he entered in 1897. Later he went to King's College and was awarded the Sambrooke Exhibition in 1906. He came to the Hospital in 1909 and obtained the M.R.C.S., L.R.C.P., in 1912, when he was appointed House Surgeon and later House Physician. In 1914 he joined the R.A.M.C., and on August 5 he went to France with the 1st General Hospital. After serving at the Base he joined a regiment in the first Battle of Ypres and later, after temporary illness, was appointed to

Hospital Barges. He returned to England on sick leave and in 1916 was posted to Mesopotamia and served there with the 3rd Lahore Division until the end of the war in 1918. After taking the F.R.C.S. in 1921 he became Clinical Assistant in the Ear, Nose, and Throat Department at King's. In 1924 he was awarded the Gold Medal at the M.S. examination of the University of London and in the same year became appointed Junior Surgeon in the Nose and Throat Department, becoming Surgeon in 1931. On the retirement of Charles Hope in 1940 Victor Negus became Senior Surgeon of the Ear, Nose, and Throat Department, and in 1946 he was appointed Active Consulting Surgeon to the department.

At the Royal College of Surgeons Victor Negus became Arris and Gale Lecturer (1924), Hunterian Professor (1925), and was awarded the John Hunter Medal and Triennial Prize (1925–7). In 1948 he was co-opted a member of the Council of the Royal College of Surgeons in order to represent Oto-laryngology.

Victor Negus was President of the Listerian Society in 1939–40 and 1940–1; he has also been President of the Lawn Tennis Club at King's. He is a past President of the Section of Laryngology, Royal Society of Medicine. He was appointed President of the International Congress of Oto-laryngology which was held at King's College, London, in July 1949.

He, with Sir St. Clair Thomson, published *The Mechanism of the Nose and Throat*. He has also contributed articles on Rhinology and Laryngology to British and foreign medical journals.

ALEXANDER CROYDON PALMER (b. 1887), O.B.E., M.B., B.S. (1913), F.R.C.S. (1913), F.R.C.O.G. (1929).

Alexander Palmer received his medical education at the University of Otago and at the London Hospital, from which he obtained the M.R.C.S., L.R.C.P., in 1910. He was House Surgeon, Pathological Assistant, Resident Accoucheur, and later Obstetric Registrar and Tutor at the London Hospital. Alexander Palmer was appointed Junior Obstetric and Gynaecological Surgeon at King's in 1925, becoming Surgeon in 1932 and Active Consulting Obstetric and Gynaecological Surgeon in 1946. He is also Surgeon at the Samaritan Free Hospital for Women.

During the war (1914–18) Alexander Palmer was Major in charge of the Surgical Division, 32nd Stationary Hospital, B.E.F., and during the war (1939–45) he was Surgeon at the Horton Emergency Hospital.

When at the London Hospital he became an English International for Rugby Football in 1908–9. At King's he took great interest in the Rugby Football Club and was for some years President of the Club (see p. 167).

He has contributed articles on gynaecology in the *Proceedings of the Royal Society of Medicine* and medical journals.

HUGH AUGUSTINE RICHARDS (1884–1949), M.A. Cantab., M.R.C.S., L.R.C.P., D.A. (1936), F.F.A., R.C.S. (1948).

Hugh Richards was educated at Rossall, at Clare College, Cambridge, and at King's College Hospital Medical School; he obtained the M.R.C.S., L.R.C.P., in 1913. From 1914 to 1916 he was Surgeon H.M. Troopships, and from 1916 to 1920 Temporary Captain, R.A.M.C., when he served in France. During his student days Hugh Richards played hockey for King's and when he returned to King's in 1920 he became prominent in resuscitating the Hockey Club. In 1926 he became Treasurer of the Clubs' and Societies' Union, an office which he filled until 1931, and in 1940 he was appointed President of the Union which flourished under his shrewd management.

Hugh Richards was Resident House Anaesthetist at King's from January to December 1920; in 1921 he was appointed Junior Anaesthetist and Lecturer on Anaesthetics; in 1929 he became Senior Anaesthetist. He retired from his appointment at King's in December 1946, and became Consulting Anaesthetist to the Hospital. He was also Consulting Anaesthetist to the City Road Lying-in Hospital.

Hugh Richards was a member and past President of the Anaesthetic Section of the Royal Society of Medicine. He wrote *Anaesthetics in Obstetrics*.

He died, while on holiday at Grenada, British West Indies, on January 22, 1949.

KING'S COLLEGE HOSPITAL AND THE MEDICAL SCHOOL, 1947

In December 1946 three appointments on the staff of the Hospital were made, but they were to date from January 1, 1947:

Samuel Oram, M.D. Lond., M.R.C.P., to be Assistant Physician and Medical Tutor.

Alexander J. Heriot, M.S. Lond., F.R.C.S., Assistant Surgeon and Surgical Tutor.

Roland Swaine Lewis, M.B., B.Ch., F.R.C.S., of St. George's Hospital, to be Assistant Surgeon in the Ear, Nose, and Throat Department.

Samuel Oram previously had been awarded a Raymond Gooch Scholarship and later the Burridge Prize in 1939 when he became Senior Scholar in the Medical School. In 1941 he was awarded the Gold Medal at the M.D. University of London. He had been Sambrooke Medical Registrar, and during the war (1939–45) was a Lieut.-Col., R.A.M.C.

Alexander Heriot had been awarded the Burridge Prize and the Legg Prize in 1936, and the next year he became Cheyne Prizeman and Senior Scholar in the Medical School. Later he was Sambrooke Surgical Registrar.

During the year other appointments and additions to the staff were made. Hubert L.-C. Wood, M.S., F.R.C.S., who had been Assistant Orthopaedic Surgeon for more than seven years, was appointed Orthopaedic Surgeon and Assistant Director of the X-Ray Department. Stanley G. Clayton, M.D., M.S., F.R.C.S., M.R.C.O.G., who had been Sambrooke Exhibitioner in 1929, Hallett Prizeman at the Royal College of Surgeons in 1931, and awarded the Jelf Medal and Todd Prize at King's in 1934, was appointed Assistant Obstetric and Gynaecological Surgeon and Tutor in Obstetrics and Gynaecology. Previously he had been Obstetric and Gynaecological Registrar.

David I. Williams, M.B., B.S., M.R.C.P., previously Registrar in the Skin Department, was appointed Assistant Physician for Diseases of the Skin. During the war (1939–45) he was a Lieut.-Col., R.A.M.C., and Adviser in Venereology, C.M.F.

J. Denis N. Hill, M.B., B.S., M.R.C.P., D.P.M., Physician at the Maudsley Hospital, was appointed Physician to the Department of

Psychological Medicine, and Herbert A. C. Mason, M.B., B.S., D.P.M., also at the Maudsley Hospital, was appointed Psychotherapist at King's.

Henry A. Magnus, M.D. Lond., Morbid Anatomist at the Hospital, was appointed Director of the Pathological Department in succession to Edward ff. Creed who died in September. A. Clegg Cunliffe, M.B., B.Ch. Cantab., was appointed Assistant Bacteriologist and Lecturer in Bacteriology. Alec H. Baynes, B.Sc., M.A., M.B., B.Ch., became acting Clinical Pathologist and Demonstrator of Pathology.

Charles H. Gray, M.Sc., M.B., B.S., F.R.I.C., Biochemist at the Hospital, was appointed Lecturer in Biochemistry in the Medical School.

In November Thomas Standring, M.D. Lond., D.P.H., a member of Gray's Inn and Medical Officer of Health for the Woolwich Metropolitan Borough, was appointed Lecturer in Public Health in the Medical School. He had been Gynaecological House Surgeon at King's and during the war (1939–45) was a Lieut.-Col., R.A.M.C.

Aubrey M. Rackow, B.Sc., M.B., B.S., D.M.R.E., was appointed Assistant Radiologist; previously he had been Resident Radiologist at the Hospital.

In January 1947 W. E. Coe retired after twenty-five years' service as Honorary Dental Surgeon and Lecturer on Operative Dental Surgery. He was appointed Consulting Dental Surgeon to the Hospital.

In September H. Audley Lucas, who had been Clinical Pathologist and Pathological Tutor since 1921, resigned.

At the end of October John Bell Milne, after twenty-four years of service, retired from the office of Dental Surgeon and Director of the Dental Department of the Hospital and Dental School; he was appointed Consulting Dental Surgeon.

At the Royal College of Surgeons J. Sim Wallace (see *King's*, p. 355), Thomas W. Widdowson (see *King's*, p. 370; also p. 88), and Ralph Cocker were elected to the Fellowship of Dental Surgery.

The following honours were bestowed upon 'King's' people during 1947: Aldwyn B. Stokes, B.M., B.Ch., M.R.C.P., Medical Superintendent at the Maudsley Hospital, received the C.B.E., and E. Stanley Merrett, B.M., B.Ch., Pathologist in Nigeria, the O.B.E.

Selwyn F. Taylor, B.M., M.Ch., F.R.C.S., was awarded the George Herbert Hunt Travelling Scholarship by the University of Oxford.

At the London University in the M.B., B.S. examination J. L. Gowans obtained honours in Pathology and Medicine; and J. Daphne M. Baker, honours in Surgery.

During the year T. Keith Lyle became appointed Civil Consultant in Ophthalmology to the Royal Air Force and in the Birthday Honours List of June 1949 he was awarded the C.B.E.

During 1947 salaried part-time Directors of Studies were appointed. In Medicine: Terence East; in Surgery: Sir Cecil P. G. Wakeley; in Obstetrics and Gynaecology: John H. Peel; and in Child Health: Wilfrid Sheldon.

Some full-time appointments were also made: R. D. Clay, B.Sc., M.B., B.S., in the Department of Morbid Anatomy; C. D. Langton, M.B., B.S., F.R.C.S., in the Orthopaedic Department; G. B. Locke, M.B., Ch.B., D.M.R.Diag., in the X-Ray Department, and B. E. Brocks, M.B., Ch.B., in the Physical Treatment Department.

In the Dental Department the new appointments were: Ralph Cocker, M.B., Ch.B. Manch., L.D.S., Director of the Dental Department and of the Dental School, Dental Surgeon to the Hospital and Sub-Dean of the Dental School; W. F. Collyer, L.D.S., to be Lecturer in Operative Dental Surgery, and K. P. Liddelow, L.D.S., H.D.D., to be Lecturer in Dental Prosthetics and Dental Materials.

Towards the end of the year an association was formed between King's and two neighbouring hospitals: The Royal Eye Hospital, St. George's Circus, and the Belgrave Hospital for Children. Under the National Health Service Act of 1948 these two hospitals have become attached to King's.

The two representatives of the Royal Eye Hospital on the Committee of Management of King's are E. A. Dorrell, F.R.C.S., and L. H. Savin, M.D., M.S., M.R.C.P., F.R.C.S., and the two representatives of the Belgrave Hospital for Children on the Committee of Management of King's are Major L. M. E. Dent, D.S.O., and R. A. Ramsay, M.A., M.Ch., F.R.C.S. The Hon. Mrs. Anthony Henley and Sir Cecil P. G. Wakeley represent King's on the Managing Committees of these two hospitals.

On February 26, 1947, the first post-war Annual Dinner of Past and Present Students of the Medical School was held; John B. Hunter occupied the chair. The toast of the Medical School and Hospital was proposed by Sir Heneage Ogilvie, K.B.E., of Guy's, a Vice-President of the Royal College of Surgeons. Terence Cawthorne, the Dean, replied. During the evening a presentation was made to S. C. Ranner on his retirement from the post of Secretary of the Medical School, a post which he had occupied with loyalty and devotion to King's for thirty-two years (see p. 137). Ranner retired in March and was succeeded by W. F. Gunn, LL.B., F.C.I.S., lately Clerk of the Faculty of Medicine of the University of Glasgow and formerly of King's College, London.

During the year F. F. Cartwright, Anaesthetist to the Hospital and Assistant Secretary to King's College Hospital Lodge, became Chairman of King's College Hospital *Gazette* Committee in succession to St. John D. Buxton, who had previously been Chairman for many years.

On October 3 the first official opening ceremony of the Medical School since 1931 took place (see *King's*, p. 373). It was the 118th Winter Session of the School and Sir Cecil P. G. Wakeley presided. The Dean, Terence Cawthorne, presented the scholars and prize-winners to Sir Edward Mellanby, K.C.B., M.D., F.R.S., Secretary of the Medical Research Council, who delivered the Inaugural Address.

At that period, October 1947, there were 312 students in the Medical School, of whom 105 were engaged in their pre-clinical studies at King's College, London.

An Intensive Postgraduate Course was held on October 4 and 5; it was attended by eighty former students of the Medical School and by some of the local practitioners.

Professor Arthur Whitfield died on January 31, 1947, aged 78. He devoted himself to dermatology, in which he paid attention to detail; this made him an outstanding teacher. During the war(1914–18) he assisted in the work at King's by acting as Physician to Out-patients as well as carrying on the work of the Dermatological Department (see *King's*, p. 417).

Frederic F. Burghard, C.B., died in Cambridge on October 31. He retired from King's in 1923, when he was appointed Consulting Surgeon (see *King's*, p. 385).

Sir Henry Lennington Martyn, K.C.V.O., late Surgeon Apothecary to H.M. Household at Windsor, died on January 7 (see *King's*, p. 317).

Harold A. Moody, M.D. Lond., died in May. He was a former Medallist, Prizeman, and distinguished athlete in the Medical School (1906–11). He became much respected by all sections of the community in south London where he was in practice. He was Chairman of the London Missionary Society in 1943.

EDWARD FFOLLIOTT CREED (1893–1947), M.A., D.M. Oxon. (1927), F.R.C.P. (1932), D.P.H. (1922).

Edward Creed received his early education at Wyggeston School, Leicester. In 1910 he entered Trinity College, Oxford, as a Millard Scholar and he obtained honours in the Final School of Natural

Science in 1913. In 1915 he came to King's and was awarded a 'Burney Yeo Scholarship'. In 1916 he took the B.M. degree and was appointed House Physician; later during the war (1914–18) he became Captain in the R.A.M.C. and worked on malaria in Sierra Leone. On his return from service in 1920 Creed was appointed Bacteriologist at King's, Lecturer on Bacteriology in the Medical School, and acting Director of the Pathological Department during the illness of Walter D'Este Emery (see *King's*, p. 397). In 1923 he became Director of the Department and Director of Pathological Studies in the Medical School, a post which he fulfilled until his death. Edward Creed was chiefly interested in bacteriology, but he was attracted to haematology and carried out research work on acholuric jaundice. During the war (1939–45) Creed was Sector Pathologist in the E.M.S., Ministry of Health. He was Examiner in Pathology in the Universities of Cambridge and London, and to the Conjoint Board.

Edward ff. Creed was director of the Pathological Department of King's for twenty-four years; he died after a short illness on September 27, 1947.

HARRY AUDLEY LUCAS, B.A. Cantab., M.R.C.S., L.R.C.P. (1914).

Audley Lucas went to the Middlesex Hospital from Trinity College, Cambridge, in 1910, and after becoming qualified he was appointed House Surgeon to Sir Alfred Pierce-Gould.

During the war from 1914 to 1920 he was a member of the R.A.M.C. and on duty with the 3rd London General Hospital, later in the 51st Highland Division, then with No. 5 General Hospital, Rouen, where he became Major and Registrar, and later with No. 3 General Hospital on the Rhine. In 1920 Lucas came to K.C.H. and was appointed House Surgeon in the Ear, Nose, and Throat Department; later he was general House Surgeon.

In 1921 he was appointed Assistant Pathologist at King's, later becoming Clinical Pathologist and Pathological Tutor. During his tutorship he was of the greatest assistance to the students in their pathological work. In 1930 he was appointed Lecturer in Pathology and Bacteriology in the Dental School. In 1931 he was appointed Sub-Dean of the Medical School and in 1932 he became Vice-Dean, an office which he held until 1937.

When the two Squash Racquets Courts were being arranged and built and were opened at King's in 1933, Lucas was prominent in all the negotiations and in the organization of the Squash Club.

He retired from King's in 1947. Lucas was Pathologist to the Institute of Laryngology and Otology Postgraduate School in connexion with the Royal National Throat, Nose, and Ear Hospital.

JOHN BELL MILNE (b. 1879), L.D.S., R.C.S. Edin. (1907), F.D.S.

Bell Milne was educated at Haries Academy, Dundee, and he served an apprenticeship in mechanical dentistry from 1897 to 1902. He studied at St. Andrews University, 1902–5, and at the Edinburgh School of Medicine and Dental Hospital, 1905–7. He was in dental practice in Dundee from 1908 to 1923 and became Lecturer and Examiner in Operative Dental Surgery at the St. Andrews University, Dundee Dental Hospital, from 1916 to 1923.

Bell Milne came to King's in 1923 when the new School of Dental Surgery was opened; he was appointed Lecturer on Dental Mechanics. In 1930 the work in the Dental School was rearranged; Bell Milne was appointed Lecturer in Prosthetics and with others he was appointed Assistant Dental Surgeon at K.C.H. In 1932 he was appointed to be in charge of the Dental Department under the direction of the Dean. He retired from his post at King's in 1947, when he was appointed Consulting Dental Surgeon to the Hospital.

When in Scotland, Bell Milne was the High Jump Champion from 1897 to 1906, except in the year 1902, and he was a member of the Scottish Athletic teams from 1897 to 1907. He represented Edinburgh University Athletic Club in the Inter-University Sports in 1906 and 1907, winning the high jump. He represented Great Britain in the Olympic Games in 1908.

While at King's, Bell Milne took a great interest in the Medical School Athletic Club.

SIDNEY CHARLES RANNER, M.A. Cantab.

On May 1, 1915, Sidney Ranner commenced his duties at King's when he was appointed Secretary of King's College Hospital Medical School in succession to Clifton Kelway.

Ranner's previous work was in the Administrative Department of King's College, Cambridge, in the course of which he gained a wide experience in the general administration of a Cambridge college.

On the death of Captain H. S. Tunnard (see *King's*, p. 248), Ranner was asked by Viscount Hambleden, Chairman of the Committee of Management of the Hospital, to carry out the duties of Secretary of the Hospital for a time; this he did throughout the winter, 1917–18. During that period Ranner accepted the post of Secretary to the

London Inter-Collegiate Scholarships Board, an appointment which he held until 1939.

Ranner gave loyal and devoted service to the Medical School and that with increased responsibilities and longer hours on duty during the war (1939–45).

In March 1947 he retired, but agreed to continue his work in the Medical School Office until the end of September in order to help the newly appointed Secretary, W. F. Gunn.

Sidney Ranner was Guest of Honour at a dinner of Past and Present Students of the Medical School with John B. Hunter as Chairman, which was held in February 1947.

Ranner was presented with a cheque and a radio-gramophone from members of the medical staff and past and present students of King's as a token of appreciation of his long and valuable service to the Medical School.

After September 1947 Sidney C. Ranner went back to reside in Cambridge. Later he joined Fitzwilliam House and Westcott House, and on December 18, 1949, he was ordained by the Bishop of Ely in St. Mary the Great, Cambridge.

KING'S COLLEGE HOSPITAL AND KING'S COLLEGE HOSPITAL MEDICAL SCHOOL, 1948

DURING the year some new appointments were made to the staff of the Hospital and to the teaching staff of the Medical School.

Harland Rees, M.Ch. Oxon., F.R.C.S., Surgical Registrar at Charing Cross Hospital and recently Resident Surgical Officer at St. Peter's Hospital, was appointed Assistant Urological Surgeon; William Paton Cleland, M.B., B.S. (Adelaide), M.R.C.P., F.R.C.S., recently Surgeon of the E.M.S. Chest Unit at Horton Hospital, was appointed Assistant Thoracic Surgeon; and Mary Juliet Wilmers, M.D. Lond., M.R.C.P., who had held the post of Registrar in the Children's Department and more recently had been the First Assistant in that department, was appointed Assistant Physician for Diseases of Children. This is the first occasion on which a woman has been elected a member of the honorary medical staff at King's.

Peter Pringle, LL.B. Lond., M.R.C.S., L.R.C.P., Barrister-at-Law, Middle Temple, Honorary Secretary of the Association of Industrial Medical Officers and a former House Surgeon at King's, was appointed Lecturer in Industrial Medicine in the Medical School. G. F. M. Hall, M.B., Ch.B., was appointed Assistant Morbid Anatomist, W. M. Davidson, M.B., Ch.B., was appointed Clinical Pathologist, A. H. Baynes, B.Sc., M.B., B.Ch., was appointed Demonstrator in Chemical Pathology, and E. Rosenstiel, L.D.S., Univ. of Manch., Assistant Lecturer in Operative Dental Surgery.

In July Hugh W. Davies, D.M. Oxon., Honorary Director of the X-Ray Diagnostic Department, resigned; he had been Honorary Radiologist at the Hospital and Lecturer in Radiology in the Medical School since 1934.

THE WILTSHIRE MEMORIAL RESEARCH SCHOLARSHIP IN CARDIOLOGY

This scholarship was founded during the year to commemorate Harold Waterloo Wiltshire, D.S.O., O.B.E., Physician to K.C.H. and teacher in the Medical School from 1910 to 1925. He died in 1937 (see *King's*, p. 419).

THE LEGG MEMORIAL LECTURE

This lecture was founded in memory of Thomas Percy Legg, C.M.G., Surgeon to K.C.H. and teacher in the Medical School from 1910 to 1930. He died suddenly on October 8, 1930 (see *King's*, p. 401).

At the University of London in May 1948 Henry A. Magnus, M.D. Lond., Director of the Pathological Department in the Medical School, was appointed Professor of Pathology in the University, and Charles H. Gray, M.Sc., M.B., B.S., F.R.I.C., Lecturer in Biochemistry in the Medical School, was appointed Professor of Chemical Pathology in the University.

At the Royal College of Surgeons, Terence Cawthorne, F.R.C.S., was appointed Hunterian Professor for 1949.

Cecil H. M. Hughes (see p. 86), Hugh A. Richards (see p. 131), Vernon F. Hall (see p. 117), Frederick F. Cartwright, and Archibald H. Galley were elected to the Fellowship of the Faculty of Anaesthetists, Royal College of Surgeons.

G. F. Cale Matthews (see *King's*, p. 355), J. Bell Milne (see p. 137), John James (see *King's*, p. 355), and L. Russell Marsh (see *King's*, p. 375) were elected to the Fellowship of Dental Surgery.

During March, Alan C. T. Perkins, M.D. Lond., and D.P.H. (1927), was appointed Medical Officer of Health for Middlesex. Alan Perkins was a Warneford Scholar at King's and he obtained the M.R.C.S., L.R.C.P., in 1923 when he was appointed Senior Casualty Officer and Senior Resident Medical Officer at K.C.H. During his student days he was a prominent member of the Medical School Hockey Team (see *King's*, p. 366).

During the year Francis Edgar Stock, M.B., B.S., F.R.C.S., A.K.C., previously Sambrooke Scholar, Jelf and Todd Medallist in the Medical School in 1938, and recently Assistant Professor of Surgery in the University of Liverpool, was elected to the chair of Surgery in the University of Hong Kong.

Selwyn F. Taylor, M.A., B.M., M.Ch., F.R.C.S., a member of the Department of Surgery at the Postgraduate Medical School of London and previously Surgical Registrar at King's, was awarded a Rockefeller Fellowship for 1948-9.

On January 9 Douglas Firth died at Cambridge (see p. 111).

On March 31 Viscount Hambleden (the third) died after an operation; a memorial service was held in the Hospital Chapel on April 8 (see p. 20).

During the year, Vidal Gunson Thorpe, C.B.E., Surgeon Rear-Admiral, R.N. (retired), who qualified from King's in 1885, died (see

King's, p. 219); Elizabeth Cowper Eaves, M.D. Lond. (1925), Lecturer in Physiology in the University of Sheffield, a former student of King's, also died.

KING'S COLLEGE HOSPITAL
(DENMARK HILL, LONDON)
1948

PRESIDENT
Her Royal Highness the Duchess of Gloucester.

VICE-PRESIDENTS
Admiral of the Fleet, the Rt. Hon. Lord Chatfield,
G.C.B., O.M., K.C.M.G., C.V.O.
The Rt. Hon. The Earl of Clarendon, K.G., G.C.M.G., G.C.V.O.
Sir Henry Gooch, J.P.
The Lord Gorell, C.B.E., M.C.
The Dowager Viscountess Hambleden.
The Lord Iliffe, C.B.E.
The Principal of King's College.
A. D. Power, F.K.C.
Claud P. Serocold, O.B.E.
Sir Percy Shepherd, C.C.
The Rt. Hon. Viscount Ullswater, G.C.B.
G. B. Williams.

1948

THE COMMITTEE OF MANAGEMENT
to July 5th

EX-OFFICIO MEMBERS
R. A. Hornby (*Treasurer*).
Rev. Canon Cyril Eastaugh, M.C., M.A. (*Honorary Chaplain*).
Sir William R. Halliday, M.A., LL.D., *Principal of King's College.*
Harold C. Edwards, C.B.E., M.S., F.R.C.S., *Dean of the Medical School.*

ELECTED MEMBERS
The Marquess of Normanby, M.B.E. (*Chairman*).
Sir William Gilliatt, C.V.O., M.D., M.S., F.R.C.S., P.R.C.O.G. (*Vice-Chairman*).
Earl Beatty, D.S.C.
C. E. A. Bedwell.
Sir Charlton Briscoe, Bt., M.D., F.R.C.P.
Major the Hon. Henry R. Broughton.
P. R. Colville.
Milton V. Ely.
The Viscountess Hambleden.
The Hon. Mrs. Anthony Henley, M.B.E.

Edward Hogg.

Michael Hornby.

The Hon. Edith Smith.

Edwin Strong.

The Hon. Mrs. Charles Tufton, O.B.E.

Temple C. Twining.

REPRESENTATIVE MEMBERS

Professor A. W. Reed, M.A., D.Litt. (nominated by the University of London).

Sir Cecil P. G. Wakeley, K.B.E., C.B., D.Sc., F.R.C.S., F.R.S.Ed. (appointed by the Council of King's College).

R. D. Lawrence, M.D., F.R.C.P. } appointed by the Medical Board.
Wilfrid Sheldon, M.D., F.R.C.P. }

Major L. M. E. Dent, D.S.O. } nominated by the Belgrave Hospital
R. A. Ramsay, M.A., M.Ch., F.R.C.S. } for Children.

E. A. Dorrell, F.R.C.S. } nominated by the Royal Eye
L. H. Savin, M.D., M.S., M.R.C.P., F.R.C.S. } Hospital.

House Governor and Secretary: S. W. Barnes, F.H.A.

Sister Matron: Miss E. A. Opie, D.N. (Lond.).

1948

KING'S COLLEGE HOSPITAL MEDICAL STAFF

Consulting Physician.

[1]1908 Sir J. Charlton Briscoe, Bt., M.D., F.R.C.P., F.K.C.

Consulting Physician to the Skin Department.

1920 J. A. Drake, M.D., F.R.C.P., D.P.H.

Consulting Physician to the Physio-therapeutic Department.

1912 E. Bellis Clayton, M.B., B.Ch.

Consulting Surgeons.

1893 Peyton T. B. Beale, F.R.C.S., F.K.C.

1893 Sir G. Lenthal Cheatle, K.C.B., C.V.O., F.R.C.S., F.K.C.

Consulting Ophthalmic Surgeons.

1899 L. V. Cargill, F.R.C.S., F.K.C.

1910 H. Willoughby Lyle, M.D., B.S., F.R.C.S., F.K.C.

Consulting Oto-Rhino-Laryngological Surgeon.

1914 C. W. M. Hope, O.B.E., M.D., F.R.C.S.

Consulting Orthopaedic Surgeon.

1919 Sir H. A. Thomas Fairbank, D.S.O., O.B.E., M.S., F.R.C.S.

Consulting Anaesthetists.

1914 Cecil H. M. Hughes, O.B.E., M.B., B.S., F.F.A.

1918 Ernest Playfair, M.B., M.R.C.P.

1921 H. A. Richards, M.A., M.R.C.S., L.R.C.P., F.F.A.

[1] The dates indicate the first appointment on the honorary staff of King's College Hospital.

Consulting Dental Surgeons.
[1]1930 T. W. Widdowson, F.D.S.
1930 W. E. Coe, D.M.D., L.D.S.
1930 J. Bell Milne, F.D.S.

Active Consulting Obstetric and Gynaecological Surgeons.
1916 Sir William Gilliatt, C.V.O., M.D., M.S., F.R.C.P., F.R.C.S., F.R.C.O.G.
1925 A. C. Palmer, O.B.E., M.B., B.S., F.R.C.S., F.R.C.O.G

Active Consulting Oto-Rhino-Laryngological Surgeon.
1924 V. E. Negus, M.S., F.R.C.S., F.K.C.

Active Consulting Urological Surgeon.
1919 John Everidge, O.B.E., F.R.C.S.

Physicians.
1924 Terence East, M.A., D.M., F.R.C.P.
1927 James L. Livingstone, M.D., F.R.C.P.
1935 Archibald Gilpin, M.D., F.R.C.P.
1938 J. Clifford Hoyle, M.D., F.R.C.P.
1939 R. S. Bruce Pearson, D.M., F.R.C.P.

Assistant Physician.
1947 Samuel Oram, M.D., M.R.C.P.

Neurologists.
1928 Macdonald Critchley, M.D., F.R.C.P.
1937 Professor Samuel Nevin, B.Sc., M.D., F.R.C.P.

Physician for Diseases of Children.
1928 Wilfrid P. H. Sheldon, M.D., F.R.C.P.

Assistant Physician for Diseases of Children.
1948 Mary Juliet Wilmers, M.D., M.R.C.P.

Physician for Diseases of the Skin.
1927 M. Sydney Thomson, M.A., M.D., F.R.C.P., F.R.S. (Edin.).

Assistant Physician for Diseases of the Skin.
1947 David I. Williams, M.B., B.S., M.R.C.P.

Physicians to the Diabetic Department.
1932 R. D. Lawrence, M.A., M.D., F.R.C.P.
1939 W. G. Oakley, M.A., M.D., F.R.C.P.

Physician for Psychological Medicine.
1947 J. Denis N. Hill, M.B., B.S., M.R.C.P., D.P.M.

Surgeons.
1922 Sir Cecil P. G. Wakeley, K.B.E., C.B., D.Sc., F.R.C.S., F.R.S. (Edin.),
F.K.C.
1928 John B. Hunter, C.B.E., M.C., M.A., M.Ch., F.R.C.S.
1928 Harold C. Edwards, C.B.E., M.S., F.R.C.S.
1934 A. Wallis Kendall, V.D., M.S., F.R.C.S.
1934 E. Grainger Muir, M.S., F.R.C.S.

[1] The dates indicate the first appointment on the honorary Staff of King's College
Hospital.

Assistant Surgeon.
    [1]1947 A. J. Heriot, M.S., F.R.C.S.

Assistant Thoracic Surgeon.
    1948 W. P. Cleland, M.B., B.S., M.R.C.P., F.R.C.S.

Obstetric and Gynaecological Surgeon.
    1936 J. H. Peel, M.A., B.M., B.Ch., F.R.C.S., F.R.C.O.G.

Assistant Obstetric and Gynaecological Surgeon.
    1947 S. G. Clayton, M.D., M.S., F.R.C.S., M.R.C.O.G.

Ophthalmic Surgeons.
    1931 L. H. Savin, M.D., M.S., M.R.C.P., F.R.C.S.
    1938 T. Keith Lyle, M.A., M.D., M.Ch., M.R.C.P., F.R.C.S.

Oto-Rhino-Laryngological Surgeons.
    1928 W. I. Daggett, M.A., M.B., B.Ch., F.R.C.S.
    1932 Terence E. Cawthorne, F.R.C.S.

Assistant Oto-Rhino-Laryngological Surgeon.
    1947 R. S. Lewis, M.B., B.Ch., F.R.C.S.

Orthopaedic Surgeons.
    1922 St. John D. Buxton, M.B., B.S., F.R.C.S.
    1931 H. Lyon-Cambell Wood, M.S., F.R.C.S.

Urological Surgeon.
    1930 J. G. Yates Bell, M.B., B.S., F.R.C.S.

Assistant Urological Surgeon.
    1948 Harland Rees, M.A., B.M., B.Ch., F.R.C.S.

Anaesthetists.
    1931 V. F. Hall, M.R.C.S., L.R.C.P., F.F.A.
    1935 F. F. Cartwright, M.R.C.S., L.R.C.P., F.F.A.

Assistant Anaesthetist.
    1939 A. H. Galley, M.B., B.S., F.F.A.

Radiological Department.
    1934 E. W. H. Shawcross, M.A., M.R.C.S., L.R.C.P., D.M.R.E. Radiologist
        for X-Ray Therapy.
    1937 A. M. Rackow, M.B., B.S., D.M.R.E., Assistant Radiologist.

Dental Surgeons.
    1930 John James, F.D.S.
    1932 L. Russell Marsh, F.D.S.
    1935 A. S. Moore, L.D.S.
    1935 W. N. L. Wade, L.D.S.
    1947 Ralph Cocker, M.B., Ch.B., F.D.S.

Assistant Dental Surgeon.
    1946 J. J. D. King, Ph.D., F.D.S.

Dental Radiologist.
    1936 R. E. Clarke, L.D.S., H.D.D. (Edin.).

    [1] The dates indicate the first appointment on the honorary Staff of King's College
Hospital.

Physical Treatment Department.
1946 Frank S. Cooksey, o.b.e., m.d., d.Phys.Med., Director.
1937 H. T. Flint, d.sc., m.r.c.s., l.r.c.p., d.m.r.e., Consulting Physicist.

Venereological Department.
1947 David I. Williams, m.b., b.s., m.r.c.p., Director.
1930 Lynette Hemmant, m.a., m.r.c.s., l.r.c.p., Assistant.
1947 Philip S. Silver, m.r.c.s., l.r.c.p., Assistant.

Pathological Department.
1946 Professor Henry A. Magnus, m.d., Director and Morbid Anatomist.

Chemical Pathology Department.
1938 Professor Charles H. Gray, m.sc., m.b., b.s., f.r.i.c., Director and
      Biochemist.

The date July 5, 1948, indicates the end of an epoch in the history
of King's College Hospital and the Medical School. Under the provisions of the National Health Act, King's College Hospital Medical
School (University of London) has its own Charter and has become
separated from King's College Hospital in all matters of administration. The Medical School is now governed by its own Council.

King's College Hospital was founded in 1839 on the initiative of
the Council of King's College, London, in order to provide clinical
instruction for the students in the Medical Department of the
College.

In matters of administration from 1839 to 1908 the Medical School
and Hospital were governed by the Council of King's College, but
from 1908 to early July 1948 the two institutions were governed by
the Committee of Management of the Hospital.

The Hospital is now designated a Teaching Hospital by the
Ministry of Health, and with it have been incorporated the Royal
Eye Hospital, St. George's Circus, and the Belgrave Hospital for
Children.

The Hospital is now managed by a Board of Governors responsible
to the Ministry of Health.

During the year the neurological, dermatological, and some of the
general medical in-patients, under the care of the medical staff of
King's have occupied wards in the Dulwich Hospital, where students
of the Medical School have been instructed. Each medical clerk in turn
now becomes a resident in the Dulwich Hospital for two weeks during
his or her six-months' appointment in the Obstetric and Gynaecology
Department at King's. Each student, working in the Children's
Department at King's, spends two weeks in residence at the Belgrave
Hospital in order to obtain some practical experience in the diseases
common to children.

L

KING'S COLLEGE HOSPITAL
Board of Governors

When the National Health Service was established in July 1948 the Minister of Health constituted a new board of governors for each of the London teaching hospitals. The boards include members appointed on the nomination of the University of London, the Metropolitan Regional Hospital Boards, and the medical teaching staffs of the hospitals.

The Board of Governors of King's College Hospital is constituted as follows:

The Marquess of Normanby, M.B.E. (*Chairman*) to hold office until March 1951.

(*a*) These to retire in March 1950 :

E. R. Cyples; Arthur Hague-Winterbotham; G. Hart; H. Lock Kendall; Hon. Mrs. Charles Tufton, O.B.E.; S. J. Worsley, D.S.O., M.C.; Ralph Cocker, M.B., Ch.B., F.D.S.; C. F. Terence East, D.M., F.R.C.P.; and H. Lyon-Cambell Wood, M.S., F.R.C.S.

(*b*) These to retire in March 1951:

Thomas H. Barr; P. R. Colville; L. M. E. Dent, D.S.O.; Milton V. Ely; Viscountess Hambleden; Hon. Mrs. Sylvia Henley, M.B.E.; J. R. H. Turton, M.B., B.S., F.R.C.S.; Wilfrid P. H. Sheldon., M.D., F.R.C.P.; and Sir Cecil P. G. Wakeley, K.B.E., C.B., F.R.C.S.

(*c*) These to retire in March 1952:

M. V. Courage; R. A. Hornby; Mrs. Mary Ormerod; J. T. Pyne; Harold C. Edwards, C.B.E., M.S., F.R.C.S.; Sir William Gilliatt, K.C.V.O., M.D., M.S., F.R.C.O.G.; J. B. Hunter, C.B.E., M.C., M.Ch., F.R.C.S.; R. D. Lawrence, M.D., F.R.C.P. and J. H. Peel, B.M., F.R.C.S., F.R.C.O.G.

KING'S COLLEGE HOSPITAL MEDICAL SCHOOL
(UNIVERSITY OF LONDON)
July 1948

King's College Hospital Medical School is a Body Corporate under the name of King's College Hospital Medical School (University of London) and the government of the School is vested in the Governing Body of the Medical School called the Council.

The Constitution of the Council

The Council consists of persons appointed in the following manner:

Four nominated by the Board of Governors of King's College Hospital:

The Marquess of Normanby, M.B.E.

R. A. Hornby.

P. R. Colville.

Milton V. Ely.

Two nominated by the Senate of the University:

Professor S. J. Davies, D.Sc., M.I.Mech.E.

Sydney T. Shovelton, C.B.E., M.A., F.K.C.

Five nominated by the Academic Board, one of whom is a representative member of the Dental Council:

S. G. Clayton, M.D., M.S., F.R.C.S., M.R.C.O.G.

T. Keith Lyle, M.A., M.D., M.Ch., M.R.C.P., F.R.C.S.

Professor H. A. Magnus, M.D.

Samuel Oram, M.D., M.R.C.P.

W. N. L. Wade, L.D.S.

The Principal of King's College, London:

Sir William R. Halliday, M.A., LL.D.

The Dean and Vice-Dean of the Medical School:

Harold C. Edwards, C.B.E., M.S., F.R.C.S., Dean.

Vernon F. Hall, M.R.C.S., L.R.C.P., F.F.A., Vice-Dean.

The Sub-Dean of the Dental School:

Ralph Cocker, M.B., Ch.B., F.D.S.

Two persons, not being members of the teaching staff of the School, co-opted by the Council:

Cyril E. A. Bedwell.

In 1949 Sir William Gilliatt, having retired from the active Hospital Staff and from the teaching staff of the Medical School, was co-opted a member of the Council.

KING'S COLLEGE HOSPITAL MEDICAL SCHOOL

(UNIVERSITY OF LONDON)

1948

DEAN

Harold C. Edwards, C.B.E., M.S., F.R.C.S.

VICE-DEAN

Vernon F. Hall, M.R.C.S., L.R.C.P., F.F.A.

SUB-DEAN OF THE DENTAL SCHOOL

Ralph Cocker, M.B., Ch.B., F.D.S.

SECRETARY

W. F. Gunn, LL.B., F.C.I.S.

THE TEACHING STAFF

Medicine.
  Terence East, M.A., D.M., F.R.C.P. (*Director*).
  James L. Livingstone, M.D., F.R.C.P.
  Archibald Gilpin, M.D., F.R.C.P.
  Clifford Hoyle, M.D., F.R.C.P.
  R. S. Bruce Pearson, D.M., F.R.C.P.
  Samuel Oram, M.D., M.R.C.P. (*Tutor*).

Cardiology.
  Terence East, M.A., D.M., F.R.C.P.

Neurology.
  Macdonald Critchley, M.D., F.R.C.P.
  Professor S. Nevin, B.Sc., M.D., F.R.C.P.

Diseases of Children and Child Health.
  Wilfrid P. H. Sheldon, M.D., F.R.C.P. (*Director*).
  Mary J. Wilmers, M.D., M.R.C.P.

Dermatology.
  M. Sydney Thomson, M.D., F.R.C.P., F.R.S. (Edin.).
  David I. Williams, M.B., B.S., M.R.C.P.

Diabetic Department.
  R. D. Lawrence, M.A., M.D., F.R.C.P.
  W. G. Oakley, M.D., F.R.C.P.

Psychological Medicine.
  Denis Hill, M.B., M.R.C.P., D.P.M.

Surgery.
  Sir Cecil P. G. Wakeley, K.B.E., C.B., D.Sc., F.R.C.S. (*Director*).
  John B. Hunter, C.B.E., M.C., M.Ch., F.R.C.S.
  Harold C. Edwards, C.B.E., M.S., F.R.C.S.
  A. Wallis Kendall, M.S., F.R.C.S.
  E. Grainger Muir, M.S., F.R.C.S.
  A. J. Heriot, M.S., F.R.C.S. (*Tutor*).

Thoracic Surgery.
  W. P. Cleland, M.B., B.S., M.R.C.P., F.R.C.S.

Urology.
  J. G. Yates Bell, M.B., B.S., F.R.C.S.
  Harland Rees, M.A., B.M., B.Ch., F.R.C.S.
    with the assistance of
  John Everidge, O.B.E., F.R.C.S.

Orthopaedics.
  St. John D. Buxton, M.B., B.S., F.R.C.S.
  H. L.-C. Wood, M.S., F.R.C.S.

Obstetrics and Gynaecology.
J. H. Peel, M.A., B.M., F.R.C.S., F.R.C.O.G. (*Director*).
S. G. Clayton, M.D., M.S., F.R.C.S., M.R.C.O.G. (*Tutor*).
  with the assistance of
Sir William Gilliatt, K.C.V.O., M.D., M.S., F.R.C.S., F.R.C.O.G.
A. C. Palmer, O.B.E., M.B., B.S., F.R.C.S., F.R.C.O.G.

Ophthalmology.
L. H. Savin, M.D., M.S., M.R.C.P., F.R.C.S.
T. Keith Lyle, M.A., M.D., M.Ch., M.R.C.P., F.R.C.S.

Oto-Rhino-Laryngology.
W. I. Daggett, M.B., B.Ch., F.R.C.S.
Terence Cawthorne, F.R.C.S.
R. S. Lewis, M.A., M.B., F.R.C.S.
  with the assistance of
V. E. Negus, M.S., F.R.C.S.

Anaesthetics.
Vernon F. Hall, M.R.C.S., L.R.C.P., F.F.A.
F. F. Cartwright, M.R.C.S., L.R.C.P., F.F.A.
A. H. Galley, M.B., B.S., F.F.A.

Dental Surgery.
Ralph Cocker, M.B., Ch.B., F.D.S. (*Director*).
John James, F.D.S.
L. Russell Marsh, F.D.S.
A. S. Moore, L.D.S.
W. N. L. Wade, L.D.S.
J. J. D. King, Ph.D., F.D.S.
E. Rosenstiel, L.D.S.

Dental Radiology.
R. E. Clarke, L.D.S., H.D.D. (Edin.).

Radio-therapy.
E. W. H. Shawcross, M.A., M.R.C.S., L.R.C.P., D.M.R.E.

Physio-therapy.
F. S. Cooksey, O.B.E., M.D., D.Phys.M. (*Director*).

Pathology and Morbid Anatomy.
H. A. Magnus, M.D. (*Professor and Director*).
A. C. Cunliffe, M.A., M.D. (*Lecturer in Bacteriology*).
G. F. M. Hall, M.B., Ch.B. (*Demonstrator in Morbid Anatomy*).
W. M. Davidson, M.B., Ch.B. (*Clinical Pathologist*).
Sheila Newstead, M.B., B.S., M.R.C.P. (*Assistant Clinical Pathologist*).

Chemical Pathology.
C. H. Gray, M.Sc., M.B., B.S., F.R.I.C. (*Professor and Director*).
A. H. Baynes, B.Sc., M.B., B.Ch. (*Demonstrator*).

Forensic Medicine.
A. P. L. Cogswell, M.B., B.S., Barrister-at-Law (*Lecturer*).

Tropical Medicine.

C. H. Barber, D.S.O., M.A., D.M. (*Lecturer*).

Industrial Medicine.

Peter Pringle, LL.B., M.R.C.S., L.R.C.P. (*Lecturer*).

Public Health.

Thomas Standring, M.D., D.P.H. (*Lecturer*).

THE OPENING OF THE WINTER SESSION FOR 1948–9

The opening of the 119th session of the Medical School took place on October 1. John Everidge, O.B.E., F.R.C.S., presided. The Dean, Harold C. Edwards, C.B.E., M.S., F.R.C.S., presented the scholars and special prize-winners to Professor (later Sir) Henry Cohen, M.D., F.R.C.P., Professor of Medicine in the University of Liverpool, who delivered the Inaugural Address.

The opening of the session was preceded by a service in the Hospital Chapel, which was initiated and arranged by the Rev. Dennis Boyling, Resident Chaplain. The service took place at noon and the Address was given by Canon C. Eastaugh, M.C., M.A., Honorary Chaplain to the Hospital.

On October 2 and 3 an Intensive Postgraduate Course was conducted in the Medical School Lecture Theatre. Lectures were delivered by S. G. Clayton, Macdonald Critchley, W. I. Daggett, Terence East, A. J. Heriot, Dennis Hill, Clifford Hoyle, John B. Hunter, W. G. Oakley, and Mary Wilmers.

ST. JOHN DUDLEY BUXTON (b. 1891), M.B., B.S. LOND. (1919), F.R.C.S. (1921).

In 1922 St. John Buxton was appointed Junior Orthopaedist and Junior Surgeon at King's to assist Thomas Fairbank in the Orthopaedic Department. In 1926 Buxton became Honorary Secretary of the Clubs' and Societies' Union, and from 1929 to 1947 he was Chairman of the Committee of *King's College Hospital Gazette*; he was succeeded by Frederick F. Cartwright.

In 1940 St. John Buxton joined the R.A.M.C. and went to the British Expeditionary Force in France, but after the evacuation he returned to King's and worked at Horton Hospital during the 'blitz'. Early in 1941 he went to the General Headquarters of the Middle East Force (for Libya, Egypt, Palestine, Iran, and Iraq) as Brigadier Consultant in Orthopaedic Surgery, but towards the end of 1943 he was invalided home. He returned to King's and became Regional Adviser to the E.M.S. for South-East England. In 1944 he was appointed Hunterian Professor at the Royal College of Surgeons.

Besides being Orthopaedic Surgeon and Lecturer on Orthopaedics at King's, Buxton is Orthopaedic Surgeon to the Royal Masonic Hospital and Consulting Orthopaedic Surgeon to the Royal Waterloo Hospital for Women and Children. He is Honorary Orthopaedic Surgeon to the Army and President of the Medical Defence Union. St. John Buxton is past President of the Orthopaedic Section of the Royal Society of Medicine, also past President of the British Orthopaedic Association.

He is the author of articles on Orthopaedics, also *Gun Shot Wounds of the Elbow Joint and Gun Shot Wounds of the Knee Joint*, and *Prevention of Accident and Limitation of Injury*.

CHARLES FREDERICK TERENCE EAST (b. 1894), M.A., D.M. Oxon. (1927), F.R.C.P. (1927).

Terence East was educated at Winchester and at New College, Oxford. He has also studied at Freiburg and Lausanne. During the War (1914–18) he served as Lieutenant in the Northamptonshire Regiment, being twice severely wounded. In 1919 Terence East came to King's, having been awarded a Burney Yeo Scholarship. He obtained the B.M., B.Ch., in 1921 and was appointed House Physician; in 1922 he obtained the M.R.C.P. and in the same year was awarded the Murchison Scholarship by the Royal College of Physicians. In 1923 he was appointed Medical Registrar at King's, and in the following year he was Radcliffe Travelling Fellow, University College, Oxford. In 1924 he was appointed Junior Physician, Senior Medical Tutor, Lecturer on Morbid Anatomy, and Curator of the Museum at K.C.H. In 1930 Terence East was President of the Listerian Society and in 1931 he was promoted Physician to the Hospital.

Terence East developed a particular interest in cardiology and became head of the Cardiological Department; he has written (jointly) *Recent Advances in Cardiology* and has contributed sundry articles to *King's College Hospital Gazette*. On the retirement of Douglas Firth in 1945, Terence East became Senior Physician and Director of Medical Studies in the Medical School.

East has been examiner in Medicine and Pathology for the Conjoint Board and in Medicine for the Society of Apothecaries.

ARCHIBALD GILPIN, M.D. Lond. (1931), F.R.C.P. (1938).

Archibald Gilpin was a distinguished member of the Medical School and during his student days, 1926–30, he was in the Rugby Fifteen. In 1929 he obtained the M.R.C.S., L.R.C.P., and the M.B.,

B.S. with honours in Medicine and was appointed House Physician. In 1931 he was awarded the Ferrier Prize for Postgraduate Research in Neurology, and in 1933 he was elected University of London Post-graduate Travelling Fellow when he visited Freiburg. At King's he became Senior Medical Registrar, Medical Officer in charge of the Rheumatic Clinic, and Medical Tutor. He was appointed Assistant Physician in 1935 and became Physician in 1942.

In 1948 Archibald Gilpin was elected the Archivist to the Worshipful Society of Apothecaries, also Harveian Librarian at the Royal College of Physicians.

ROBERT DANIEL LAWRENCE (b. 1892), M.A., M.D. ABERD. (1922), F.R.C.P. (1932).

R. D. Lawrence was educated at Aberdeen Grammar School and at Aberdeen University, where he was awarded the Fife Jamieson and Lizars Gold Medals in 1913 and the Shepherd and Anderson Gold Medals in 1915. He graduated M.B., Ch.B. with honours in 1916 and then served with the R.A.M.C. until 1919, when he came to K.C.H. and was appointed Casualty Officer, also House Surgeon. During the time he was in residence he was captain of the hockey team and a member of the Lawn Tennis Six. Later he worked in the Ear, Nose, and Throat Department, and when chiselling a mastoid a chip of bone damaged his cornea causing severe sepsis and, while in hospital, he was found to be diabetic. For a time he went to Italy to engage in general practice, but returned to King's in 1923 to have his life rescued by the new insulin discovery. He was appointed Bio-chemist at the Hospital in 1924 and became mainly occupied with research work particularly in connexion with the treatment of diabetes. He was also Lecturer on Biochemistry in the Medical School. These offices he held until 1932 when he was appointed Assistant Physician-in-charge of the Diabetic Department, becoming Physician in 1939 and, as a result of his work, he has developed a large department for the treatment of diabetic patients.

At the Royal Society of Medicine Lawrence has been President of the Therapeutic Section, and at the Royal College of Physicians he was Oliver-Sharpey Lecturer in 1946, and in the same year he received the presentation of the Banting Medal from America. He was President of the Listerian Society during 1947–8. Lawrence is the author of the well-known book *The Diabetic Life* which has gone through many editions; it has been translated into numerous foreign languages. He has written articles on Insulin, on Diabetes, and on Endocrinology; he also founded the Diabetic Association.

JAMES LIVINGSTONE LIVINGSTONE (b. 1900), M.D. Lond. (1925), F.R.C.P. (1933)., F.K.C. (1949).

James Livingstone was educated at Worksop College and at King's College, London, which he entered in 1917. From May 1918 to March 1919 he served in the R.N.A.S. and R.A.F. as Flight Cadet. He came to K.C.H. in 1920 and obtained the M.R.C.S., L.R.C.P., in 1922. He was appointed House Surgeon, later House Physician, and then Sambrooke Medical Registrar in 1924.

James Livingstone was a member of the Rugby First Fifteen while at the Hospital (see *King's*, pp. 371 and 473), he was also a member of the hockey team, 1921 to 1925. In 1927 he was appointed Junior Physician and Demonstrator of Pathology at King's, and when the Asthma Research Clinic was established he was appointed Director. He was President of the Listerian Society, 1932–3, and Treasurer of the Rugby Football Club, 1932–47.

In 1932 James Livingstone was appointed Assistant Physician at Brompton Hospital, becoming Physician in 1948, he is also Physician to the Royal National Hospital, Ventnor. He has served on the Council of the Royal College of Physicians from 1946 to 1948. He has published *Variations in the Volume of the Chest with Changes of Posture*, and articles on Asthma.

JOHN HAROLD PEEL, M.A., B.M., B.Ch. Oxon. (1932), F.R.C.S. (1933), F.R.C.O.G. (1944).

John Peel came to King's in 1928 from Oxford, where he had been awarded First Class Honours in Natural Science: he was awarded a Raymond Gooch Scholarship at King's. He obtained the M.R.C.S., L.R.C.P., in 1930 and then held house appointments—Assistant Casualty Officer, House Surgeon, and Senior House Accoucheur. In 1932 he was appointed Obstetric Registrar and Tutor, and later he became First Assistant in the Obstetric and Gynaecological Department at King's. For a time he was Registrar at the Samaritan Hospital for Women. In 1936 he was appointed Honorary Assistant Obstetric and Gynaecological Surgeon at King's, becoming Obstetric and Gynaecological Surgeon in 1943. He was appointed Director of the Gynaecological Department in 1948.

John Peel was President of the Listerian Society during the session 1946–7.

He is the author of a *Textbook of Gynaecology* and of articles on Obstetrics.

LEWIS HERBERT SAVIN (b. 1901), M.D. Lond. (1930), M.S. (1934), M.R.C.P. (1927), F.R.C.S. (1926).

Lewis Savin was educated at Christ's Hospital and at King's College, London, where he was awarded a Warneford Scholarship in 1918, the Warneford Prize in 1919, and the Barry Prize in 1920. He entered King's College Hospital Medical School in 1921 and obtained the M.R.C.S., L.R.C.P., in 1924. He was awarded the London University Medal at the M.S. Ophthalmology Examination.

Lewis Savin was House Surgeon, later Pathologist, Surgeon, and subsequently Senior Surgeon at the Royal Eye Hospital. In 1928 he became Medical Superintendent at the Seamen's Hospital, Greenwich, Ophthalmic Surgeon at the Metropolitan Hospital, 1929–34, and Consulting Ophthalmic Surgeon at the Maudsley Hospital, 1937–9. At the Ophthalmological Society of the United Kingdom he was Honorary Secretary, 1937–9, and a member of the Council, 1939–42. At the Royal College of Surgeons he became Hunterian Professor in 1943 and delivered the lecture 'Non-magnetizable Intra-ocular Foreign Bodies' and in 1947 he presented to the Vision Committee of the Medical Research Council a report on 'The Effect of Aluminium and its Alloys on the Eye'.

Lewis Savin was appointed Assistant Ophthalmic Surgeon at King's in 1931 and he became Senior in the department when J. Myles Bickerton retired in 1945.

He was prominent in the negotiations which resulted in a close association between K.C.H. and the Royal Eye Hospital.

He is the author of *Gullstrand's Slit-Lamp in Out-patient Work of an Eye Hospital.*

JOHN GEOFFREY YATES BELL (b. 1902), M.B., B.S. (1926), F.R.C.S. (1930).

Yates Bell was educated at St. Dunstan's and King's College, London, which he entered in 1920. He obtained the M.R.C.S., L.R.C.P., in 1925 and was appointed House Surgeon at King's. Later he became Senior Casualty Officer and in 1928 he was appointed Senior Surgical Registrar. In 1930 he was appointed on the honorary staff of the Hospital as Assistant Urological Surgeon, becoming Urological Surgeon in 1937. For a time he worked at Rokus Kurhaus Urological Clinic, Budapest. In 1924 Yates Bell was Secretary of the King's First Lawn Tennis Six, the year when King's won the Senior and the Junior Inter-Hospital Lawn Tennis Cups. He was a member of the First Six for some years (see *King's*, p. 479). He was President of the Listerian Society in 1948. During the war (1939–45) he became Senior Surgeon at the Leatherhead Emergency Hospital.

Yates Bell is a Fellow of the International Society of Urology; he was Secretary of the Urological Section of the Royal Society of Medicine (1937–8). He is the author of 'Penicillin and Prostatectomy', 'Urinary Tuberculosis in Children', and of other papers on Urinary Surgery.

The Names of some of the more distinguished Members of King's College Hospital Medical School 1939–48

Abbott, J. D.
Ackesley, A. G.
Adams, J.
Adderley, D.
Alcock, Helen B.
Allison, J. F. T.
Anderson, T. B.
Anthony, E. James.
Arneaud, J. D.
Attenborough, C. G.

Baker, Joan Daphne M.
Ball, M. J.
Barber, A. R.
Barnes, D. R.
Barnes, Helen F.
Barnett, J. D. W.
Barrett, D. H.
Beales, S. J.
Begg, W. H. B.
Belgrave, D. P.
Bell, R. S.
Bennett, Elizabeth.
Bennett, W. E. J.
Beynon, A. E.
Birchetts, S.
Bolton, V. H.
Boulton, Margaret E. M.
Bowen, Kathleen A. C.
Briggs, A. J.
Briggs, J. R.
Brock, Bevis H.
Brock, D. O.
Brocks, B. E.
Brudenell, J. M.
Bryant, L. F.

Bunn, R. G.
Burt, Joyce M.
Buxton, R. St. John.

Carruthers, K. J. M.
Carter, F.
Caton, R. D.
Cawson, R. A.
Challacombe, K. V.
Chappel, Irene M. S.
Childs, John P.
Christie, T.
Clayton, J. P.
Clover, P. T.
Coles, R. B.
Colley, Ian H.
Comyn, John (M.B.E.).
Copeland, R. L.
Copestake, I. J. H.
Cotton, L. T.
Crease, J. A.
Cule, J. H.

Dadds, J. H.
Dansie, E. R.
Davies, Brenda M.
Davies, Edith M.
Davies, Margaret E.
Davies, Roland G.
Davis, L. R.
de Silva, A. L.
de Silva, H. S.
Douglas, Joy Marjorie.
Doust, J. W. L.
Drury, Kathleen A. D.
Dunbar, Alison B.

Edmiston, D. F.
Edsall, J. R.
Elphinstone, Norah C.
Ensor, G. F.
Evans, R. Gwyn (M.B.E.).

Fearnhead, R. W.
Ferrari, R. L. M.
Franklin, J. R.

Garai, Oliver F.
Garrett, J. R.
Gillett, Raymond L.
Goodacre, Joy Kathleen.
Gowans, J. L.
Graham, J.
Grant, G.
Grant, Joyce F.
Green, S. I.
Gresham, G. A.
Griffiths, C. H.
Gun-Munro, S. D.
Gurling, K. J.

Hall, G. F. M.
Hanley, T.
Hanraty, J. A.
Hansen, Marjorie S.
Hargreaves, T.
Harris, P. C.
Harrison, I. S.
Harvey, R. M.
Hay, Ursula M.
Hayward, J. S.
Hervey, G. R.
Hinton, J. M.
Hobbs, A. A.
Hobbs, F. E.
Holmes, P. E. B.
Hooton, Norman S.
Hopewell, John P.
Hopkins, Pamela C. B.
Howell, R. D.
Howett, R. J.
Huggill, P. H.
Hunt, J. A.
Husain, O. A. N.
Huston, A. F.

Jerwood, Maragaret H.

Jesson, G.
Jörgensen, Thelma D.

Kader, L.
Kane, Iris.
Kay, C. W.
Keeping, Joyce A.
Kelham, B. H.
Kelly, R. A.
Kenny, A. John.
Kiloh, Leslie G.
Kingsley-Pillers, Elizabeth M.
Kinmont, P. D. C. (M.B.E.).
Kirman, B. H.
Klein, R. R.
Knight, R. J.

Laing, P. G.
Langford, Joan F.
Latta, A. L. O.
Leach, Barbara M.
Lees, Norman.
Leeson, C. R.
Leeson, T. S.
Leighton, B. C.
Lindley, D. C.
Loder, R. E.
Lucas, T.

Macarthur, A. M.
Macdonald, I. J.
McDowall, Elizabeth G. S.
McDowall, Janet G. S.
McVey, T.
Madge, H. E.
Madgwick, Belle Alvina.
Malkin, E. A.
Mason, M. K.
Mason, Margaret M.
Mather, Francis E.
Maxwell, Aileen N.
Mayer, M. E.
Mayo, P. D.
Meade, B. W.
Meadowcroft, Lorna M.
Melville, Stuart L.
Merrifield, A. J.
Merry, A. J.
Metcalfe, Edith M.

Middleton, J.
Millard, J. B.
Miller, H. J.
Miller, J. R. M.
Moller, Mary Hester.
Moody, Harold E. A.
Mounsey, J. P. D.

Neaves, C. H.
Newstead, Sheila M.

Oyston, Margaret G.

Parton, Hilary C.
Partridge, Margaret E. M.
Partridge, R. L.
Paterson, J. M.
Pathy, M.S.N.
Pathy, W. J.
Pease, N. J.
Pickles, Basil G.
Prendergast, Kathleen L.
Pringle, Mary.
Prior, K. G.
Pritchard, Graham C.

Randle, A. P. H.
Read, R. C.
Reynords, Muriel P.
Richards, T. A.
Rinsler, M. G.
Roberts, Colin S. C.
Rosenthal, F. F. D.
Rowell, S.
Rubie, J.
Rundle, A. J.
Rutherford, P. I.

Sampson, A. J.
Shanley, H. M. G.
Sharland, R. J.
Sharvill, D. E.
Shaw, S. R.
Shearer, J. M. L.
Sheldon, Peggy.
Shepherd, P. R.
Sibly, Alice Mary.
Simpson, Jean V.
Sloper, Irene M. S.

Smith, Audrey U.
Sneath, P. H. A.
Snell, R. Saxon.
Southwell, Madeline D.
Southwell, W. B.
Spalding, B. M.
Sparks, Joyce F.
Stanley, Douglas A.
Stephens, W. M.
Sterndale-Bennett, Winifred A.
Stewart, Ross.
Stimpson, Vera E.
Strickland, P.
Stubbings, A. C. L.
Summerhayes, J. L. V.
Sunderland, H.
Sunderland, R. A.
Sutton, F. R.

Tate, N.
Teasdale, D. H.
Terry, J.
Thomas, E. T.
Thomas, L. B.
Thompson, Greta C.
Towers, John.
Toye, D. K. M.
Trickey, E. L.
Tucker, F. G.
Tuffill, S. G.
Turtle, E. C.

Van't Hoff, Daphne G.
Vicary, P. M.

Wakely, J. H.
Walker, D. H. G.
Watson, Hazel Gwyneth.
Waugh, W.
Webb, Dinah D.
Weeks, K. F.
Weeks, R. B.
Wheatley, A. E.
Wheble, V. H.
Whittaker, H.
Wild, E. B.

Yates, G. N.

STANLEY OSBORN AYLETT, B.Sc., M.B., B.S. (1935), F.R.C.S. (1936).

Stanley Aylett entered the Medical Faculty of King's College, London, in 1929, when he was awarded a Medical Entrance Scholarship in Science. He gained the Alfred Hughes Memorial Prize in Anatomy, the Huxley Prize in Physiology, and the Jelf Medal in 1931, and in the same year he was awarded the Dunn Exhibition in Anatomy and Physiology by the University of London. In 1932 he obtained First Class Honours at the B.Sc. London University and in the same year he was awarded a Medical Entrance Scholarship at K.C.H. Medical School. In 1935 he obtained the Tanner Prize and the Legg Prize for Surgical Pathology and in the same year he passed the M.R.C.S., L.R.C.P., and the M.B., B.S., with honours in Medicine.

He was appointed House Surgeon at King's, after which he became Sambrooke Surgical Registrar.

During the time that Stanley Aylett was at King's he was a member of the Rugby First Fifteen, Vice-Captain in 1935, and Captain in 1936.

He has been Resident Surgical Officer at the Gordon Hospital and the Princess Beatrice Hospital. He is the author of *Miles's Abdominoperineal Operation, treatment before and after* and *New Diathermy Sigmoidoscope.*

JOHN VIVIAN DACIE, M.B., B.S. (1935), M.R.C.P. (1936).

John Dacie received his earlier medical education in the Medical Faculty of King's College, London, where he was awarded a Sambrooke Exhibition in 1930 and the Alfred Hughes Memorial Prize in Anatomy in 1932. At K.C.H. he obtained the Ware Prize in 1933, and the Legg Prize in Surgical Pathology in 1934; in 1935 he was awarded the Jocelyn Almond Prize and the Todd Prize, and he became Senior Scholar. After becoming qualified he was appointed House Physician at King's. During the war (1939–45) he was for a time Resident Pathologist at King's and Pathologist to the Emergency Medical Service, later he became a Major in the R.A.M.C.

He held a Medical Research Council Postgraduate Studentship in 1937, and a Will Edmonds Clinical Research Fellowship at K.C.H. in 1938.

In October 1948 John Dacie was appointed to a Readership in Haematology at the Postgraduate Medical School of London.

He is author of numerous articles on various 'blood conditions'.

One of his later articles (with P. L. Mollison) is 'Survival of Transfused Erythrocytes from a Donor with Nocturnal Haemoglobinuria' (*Lancet*, 1949).

SELWYN FRANCIS TAYLOR, M.A., B.M., B.Ch. Oxon. (1939), M.Ch. (1946), F.R.C.S. (1940).

Selwyn Taylor came to King's from Oxford University in 1936, when he was awarded a Burney Yeo Scholarship. He obtained the M.R.C.S., L.R.C.P., in 1939 and was appointed House Surgeon. Later he became Surgical Registrar. During the war (1939–45) he was Surgeon Lieut.-Commander, R.N.V.R., and was appointed Surgical Specialist. In 1947 he was awarded the George Herbert Hunt Travelling Scholarship by Oxford University. Later he became a member of the Surgical Department of the Postgraduate Medical School of London, and in 1948 he was awarded a Rockefeller Fellowship.

Selwyn Taylor was Secretary of the Listerian Society, 1937–9, and Editor of the *K.C.H. Gazette* in 1939. He is the author of 'Musicogenic Epilepsy' and 'Fracture Dislocation of Occipital Bone' (*Brit. J. Surg.*).

SECTION XII

THE CLUBS' AND SOCIETIES' UNION

1934—48

	Presidents	Treasurer	Honorary Secretaries
1934–6	C. W. M. Hope	H. L.-C. Wood	St. J. D. Buxton
1936–41	,,	,,	W. Neville L. Wade
1941–6	H. A. Richards	,,	,,
1946–7	H. C. Edwards	,,	Hugh L. Davies
1947–8	W. Neville L. Wade	,,	{ Hugh L. Davies to May 1948 David I. Williams

THE Clubs' and Societies' Union has benefited by the sum of one hundred pounds left to it by the late T. P. Legg (see *King's*, p. 401), who took a special interest in the Rugby Football Club. The funds of the Union have also been augmented by sums of money from the Medical School Dance Club (see p. 175).

THE LISTERIAN SOCIETY OF KING'S COLLEGE HOSPITAL MEDICAL SCHOOL

SESSION 1934–5

President: Macdonald Critchley

Professor J. J. Lhermitte of Paris delivered an interesting lecture on 'Charcot, His Life and Times'.

Mr. Ivor Back spoke on 'Holmes; Dr. Watson as a Medical Man'.

Others who addressed the Society were Dr. G. W. B. James on 'A Medical Study of the Life of Lenin'; Dr. W. J. O'Donovan, Dr. J. D. Rolleston, Professor E. C. Dodds, and Dr. J. H. Hunt. The Presidential Address dealt with 'The Monster of Düsseldorf: the Story of a Mass Murderer'.

SESSION 1935–6

President: Harold C. Edwards

Papers were read by Dr. H. Gerald Horner, Editor of the *British Medical Journal*, by Mr. (later Sir) G. Gordon-Taylor on 'The Spirit of Surgery', and by Sir Harold D. Gillies on 'Plastic Surgery'. Others who contributed papers were Professor Edward Mapother on

'Psychotherapy in Fact and Fancy', Dr. A. Douglas Cowburn, H.M. Coroner for South London, and Mr. Aldous Huxley. The Presidential Address was on 'Osteopathy, Chiropractic and other Healing Cults'.

SESSION 1936–7
President: Edward Mapother

Sir St. Clair Thomson delivered an address on 'A House Surgeon's Memories of Lord Lister', Professor Hugh Cairns spoke on 'Brain Surgery', and Professor E. C. Dodds on 'The Problems of Cancer Research', and Sir W. Langdon Brown on 'The Integration of the Endocrine System'. Others who addressed the Society were Dr. Alan Gregg, Medical Director of Rockefeller Foundation, on 'Psychological Research', Mr. J. G. Crowther, Mr. Guy Brown, Dr. Charles Singer, and Dr. C. E. Newman. The Presidential Address was entitled 'The Psychiatry that is coming'.

SESSION 1937–8
President: Charles E. Newman

Dr. Donald Hunter gave an address on 'Nutritional Deficiencies in Clinical Medicine', Sir Joseph Barcroft on 'Foetal Respiration', Sir Henry Gauvain on 'Surgical Tuberculosis', and Dr. Crighton Bramwell on 'The Heart in Athletes', and others who addressed the Society were Dr. Charles Singer, Dr. Zuckerman, and Dr. Harry Roberts.

SESSION 1938–9
President: Wilfrid Sheldon

Addresses were delivered by Sir Harold Gillies on 'Plastic Surgery', by Dr. Robert Hutchison on 'Medical Literature', and by Dr. Halliday Sutherland on 'The History of Tuberculin'. Others who addressed the Society were Dr. J. H. Sheldon, Dr. W. J. O'Donovan, 'The Good Estate of Medicine', and Dr. Norman Haire.

The Presidential Address on 'Juvenile Crime' was delivered before a large audience.

SESSION 1939–40
President: Victor E. Negus

The first meeting of the Society was due to take place at King's on October 18, as the members of the Society were scattered at hospitals in Surrey and were no longer available at King's, the meetings for the session were cancelled. Later a Junior Listerian Society was formed and meetings arranged.

M

Session 1946–7

President: John H. Peel

In October 1946 meetings of the Society were resumed at King's. The first speaker of the session was Brigadier Glyn Hughes, D.S.O., on 'Belsen'. Other speakers were Sir H. A. Thomas Fairbank, Professor R. R. Mackintosh, Dr. W. D. Nicol, and Mr. E. Grainger Muir.

Session 1947–8

President: R. D. Lawrence

Papers were read by Major-General Sir Edward Spears on 'The Racial and Political Problems of the Middle East', also by Professor Andrew Topping, Dr. Macdonald Critchley, Mr. Arnold Haskell, and by Mr. Howard Marshall. There were two interesting Clinical Evenings.

Office-Bearers of the Listerian Society

	Presidents	Secretaries	
1934–5	Macdonald Critchley, M.D.	B. B. Waddy	D. J. Watterson
1935–6	Harold C. Edwards, M.S.	D. I. Watterson	C. I. Murphie
1936–7	Edward Mapother, M.D.	C. I. Murphie	D. Whitteridge
1937–8	Charles Newman, M.D.	D. Whitteridge	S. F. Taylor
1938–9	Wilfrid Sheldon, M.D.	S. F. Taylor	L. D. de Launay
1939–40	Victor E. Negus, M.S.	L. D. de Launay	A. B. Kinnier Wilson
1946–7	J. H. Peel, M.B.	Ian H. Colley	Pamela C. B. Hopkins
1947–8	R. D. Lawrence, M.D.	Pamela C. B. Hopkins	J. M. L. Shearer
1948–9	J. G. Yates Bell, M.B.	J. M. L. Shearer	Joan F. Langford

THE DENTAL SOCIETY

	Presidents	Treasurers	Secretaries
1934–5	L. Russell Marsh	D. Laverick	K. H. Brattle
1935–6	John James	P. F. H. Gaskell	W. C. Allwright
1936–7	T. W. Widdowson	T. N. G. Copestake	H. G. Bynoe
1937–8	A. S. Moore	D. H. Shepperd	C. H. Griffiths
1938–9	R. E. Clarke	R. I. H. Whitlock	C. H. Vigar
1939–40	J. Bell Milne	J. Morris-Wilson	F. L. Hall
1940–1	W. N. L. Wade	G. F. Dyer	B. C. Leighton
1941–2	J. James	K. V. Challacombe	P. R. Shepherd
1942–3	W. F. Collyer	R. J. Howett	A. C. L. Stubbings
1943–4	T. W. Widdowson	Madeleine D. Southwell	P. D. Mayo

	Presidents	Treasurers	Secretaries
1944–5	L. Russell Marsh	Madeleine D. Southwell	R. J. Sharland
1945–6	A. S. Moore	D. H. Barrett	L. F. Bryant
1946–7	J. J. D. King	Daphne G. Van't Hoff	B. M. Spalding
1947–8	R. E. Clarke	Lorna M. Meadowcroft	M. E. Mager
1948–9	W. F. Collyer	Hazel G. Watson	M. E. Mager

The Dental Society Meetings are held in the Medical School; they are attended both by senior and junior members of the School. The Annual Dinner and Dance of the Society provides an enjoyable evening.

THE JUNIOR LISTERIAN SOCIETY

Meetings were held at Leatherhead Hospital and at Horton Hospital.

	Presidents	Secretaries	
1940–1	A. C. D. Firth, M.D.	A. C. Turner	V. G. Springett
1941–2	L. H. Savin, M.D., M.S.	A. C. Turner	J. P. Hopewell
1942–3	Clifford Hoyle, M.D.	J. P. Hopewell	E. M. Kingsley-Pillers
1943–4	H. L.-C. Wood, M.S.	E. M. Kingsley-Pillers	W. Waugh
1944–5	N. R. Barrett, M.Ch.	W. Waugh	Thelma D. Jörgensen
1945–6	L. S. Bruce Pearson, D.M.	Thelma D. Jörgensen	Ian H. Colley

The first meeting of the Junior Listerian Society took place on February 5, 1940, at Leatherhead, when the President delivered an address entitled 'Examinations from the Examiner's Point of View'.

THE MUSICAL SOCIETY

During the early years of the Society the meetings were held in the Board Room of the old Hospital in Portugal Street, more recently the meetings have been held in the Board Room of the present Hospital. Since the Medical School buildings were completed, the monthly meetings of the Society take place in the refectory hall of the School. During recent years the informal smoking concerts have been superseded by less frequent but more highly organized entertainments.

The President of the Society, usually elected each year, is a member of the honorary medical staff and he handles the President's Hammer which was presented to the Society by Walter d'Este Emery, when President for the session 1911–12 (see *King's*, p. 397).

The Society arranges the Christmas Shows, which until recently were presented in the Out-patients' Waiting Hall; now they are given in the Medical School.

For some time past the Society has benefited by the experience of Harry A. Lucas and Hubert L.-C. Wood in producing the Christmas entertainments. It is not possible to name all those members of the Society who have assisted in entertaining their large audiences of patients, nurses, and friends, but special mention is made of Leslie Shackleton (saxophone) and Dennis Barley for their orchestras, Leonard Hussey (see p. 122) for his banjo solos, Cyril W. Dixon for his power of organizing the stage lighting, and Stephen G. Shippard for his own particular method of entertaining.

The first production on the stage in the Medical School Refectory was *Cabbage and King's*, a revue written and produced by Charles F. C. Parkinson and Thomas C. Probyn, presented in December 1934. *Fisk and Cheer*, another revue by the same producers, was put on at Christmas 1935. There was a superb performance of *Aladdin* in December 1936; *Jack and the Beanstalk*, a distinctly comic turn, appeared in 1937; and in December 1938 *Knightmare*, an original pantomime of the Middle Ages, written by members of the Medical School, was splendidly received and the orchestra was well led by John Warrick.

In March 1939 the Society made a new and ambitious venture when *Baa, Baa, Black Sheep* was admirably presented by Esme Gillieson, and much of the success of the play was due to David I. Williams.

In December 1939 the war-time Christmas Show—*Nonsense and Stuff*—was presented, and the outstanding players were Bruce Kinnier Wilson, Tony Chalmers Turner, John Warrick, Islay Barne, Joan Cleland, and Rosa Piggot.

In addition to those already named other successful producers, managers, and conductors were: Dennis Barley, Floyd Hewlett, Robert Lattey, John Morris, John M. Naish, and John Watson.

Others who are worthy of special mention are: W. M. Anderson, Alec Baynes, J. S. G. Burns, Ronald Crick, Donald Davies, Geoffrey Doel, Philip Edmondson, Donald Macdonald, Terence Marshall, Frank Milne, Selwyn Taylor, Sidney Truelove, B. B. Waddy, Hugh Wallis, Robert Wheeler, and David Whitteridge.

Amongst the women students who have helped to make the Christmas and other shows such a success are: Mary Allardice, Monica Austin, Josephine Campbell, Christina Duigan, Hermione Eames, Joyce George, Dorothy Gibson, Ursula Hickman, Marjorie Phillips, Peggy Plews, Nora Reid, Jean Richardson, Cynthia Sandys, Margaret Stalker, Barbara Travers, Dorothy Webber, Elizabeth Western, and Celia Westropp.

On occasions Aubrey Rackow has obliged with topical songs at the meetings of the Society, and the Society has frequently had the company of James Livingstone, Terence Cawthorne, and John P. Clayton at their meetings; all of whom take a keen interest in music.

In October 1947 the Society became the 'Musical and Dramatic Society'. The Chairman elected was L. Kader and the Hon. Secretary, S. Rowell. The other members of the Committee were D. Adderly, S. Birchetts, and Ray Gillett; C. Shaw was appointed Musical Director.

At the memorial services held in the Hospital Chapel the Society has supplied the choir and, before Christmas and on Christmas Eve, the choir has toured the wards and sung to the patients.

ATHLETIC SPORTS

In 1935 the Cawthorne Cup, for the best individual performance in any event, went to S. C. Truelove, who won the mile and the half-mile. The high and long jumps were won by A. D. Hodges (see p. 111).

In 1936 C. I. Murphie won the three miles in 15 min. 54 sec.; he also won the mile and the half mile; A. J. Heriot won the 100 yards in 10·75 sec., also the 440 yards; A. D. Hodges won the long jump at 20 ft. 2·5 in. At the Inter-Hospitals Championships, King's was represented by F. M. Collins, A. J. Heriot, C. I. Murphie, R. A. Palmer, and J. W. Warrick. R. A. Palmer ran a dead-heat in the quarter mile; C. I. Murphie won the three miles and was second in the mile.

In 1937 Denis F. Glass was Captain and he won the hammer throw at 105 ft. 10 in. In the University of London Athletic Meeting he came second for the hammer throw. At the meeting in 1938 Roy Dunstan, the Captain, won the 120 yards high hurdles in 16·5 sec., the high jump at 5 ft. 4 in., also the half mile. A. J. Heriot won the 100 yards in 10·5 sec. and the quarter mile in 58·4 sec.; D. F. Glass won the weight-put at 33 ft. 11·5 in. and the hammer hurl.

At the Inter-Hospitals Championships Sports held at Motspur Park in June Roy Dunstan won the 120 yards high hurdles in 15·8 sec., also the low hurdles and the quarter mile. Denis F. Glass threw the discus 99 ft. 6 in. Of the eight competing hospitals, King's came fourth.

In 1939 the Cawthorne Cup went to D. F. Glass who threw the hammer 128 ft. 5 in. (a record for King's). H. E. A. Moody won the high jump at 5 ft. 4·5 in.; Moody also put the weight 42 ft. 3 in. (a record for King's). (In this connexion it is of interest to note that his father Harold A. Moody won the weight-put for the Medical

Department at the King's College Sports Meeting held at the old athletic ground at Wormwood Scrubbs in 1906 and also in 1907) (see p. 135). Roy Dunstan, the Captain, won the 120 yards hurdles in 15·6 sec. (a record for King's), the 440 yards, and the half mile in 2 min. 11 sec. The 100 yards and the 220 yards were won by R. Pitchford, and the mile was won by P. A. Edge. At the Southern Championships Meeting at Motspur Park in June, Roy Dunstan won the 440 yards in 56·3 sec., and at the White City International Meeting held in August King's was represented by Roy Dunstan and R. A. Palmer.

In 1947 the Sports Meeting was resumed at Dog Kennel Hill. J. M. Brudenell gave an outstanding performance; J. L. Gowans, B. S. Lush, and J. B. Millard all did well. In 1948 J. B. Millard won the half mile in 2 min. 4 sec., Rowland Leeson won the high jump at 5 ft. 6 in. (a record for King's) and the long jump at 20 ft. 9 in. P. J. Rutherford threw the cricket ball 102 yds. 1 ft. 2 in. T. Christie and H. E. A. Moody represented Great Britain in the Olympic Games.

Holders of the Victor Ludorum Cup

1935 A. D. Hodges (see p. 111)	1939 Roy Dunstan
1936 C. I. Murphie	1947 J. M. Brudenell
1937 D. F. Glass	1948 J. B. Millard
1938 Roy Dunstan	

THE RUGBY FOOTBALL CLUB

In 1913 King's played against University College Hospital in the Inter-Hospitals Cup Tie; King's lost by 13 points to nil. Of the team which represented King's, R. H. Leigh, E. D. Lindow, and Gilbert Moore played for the United Hospitals.

In 1935 King's reached the final round for the Inter-Hospitals Cup, but lost to St. Mary's by 11 points to 3.

The team was: G. R. Steed, back; S. O. Aylett (Vice-Captain), H. S. Mellows, G. S. Davis, and H. G. Bynoe, three-quarters; A. D. Hodges and T. A. M. Johns, halves; J. D. Moore (Captain), S. G. Clayton, D. F. Glass, A. P. Kitchin, S. J. Chamberlain, D. Laverick, R. J. Gilpin, and W. C. Allwright, forwards. The side was the strongest which had represented King's since that of 1926, which then included R. Cove-Smith, D. J. MacMyn, W. R. Collis, W. Neville L. Wade, C. J. Farr, and H. N. Knox. Two members of the 1935 team, J. D. Moore and D. F. Glass, played for the United Hospitals.

The members of the 1935 team which had played together throughout the Cup Competition were given silver cigarette cases, inscribed to commemorate their efforts in the Inter-Hospitals Cup Tie. The presentation was made possible by the generosity of the honorary medical staff. The cigarette cases were distributed by Alec C. Palmer (a former International player), Vice-President of the Club, who complimented the fifteen on their fine team spirit. Later Alec C. Palmer was elected President of the Club and remained in office for some years.

In 1936 Stanley O. Aylett became Captain. King's beat the London in the first round for the Cup, but lost to St. Thomas's in the second round.

In 1937 G. R. Steed was Captain, but King's again lost to St. Thomas's. In 1938 the team, captained by D. F. Glass, beat the London in the first round, drew with Guy's in the second round, but lost the replay. D. F. Glass and H. G. Bynoe played for the United Hospitals.

In 1939 D. F. Glass was again Captain. The team beat St. George's in the first round, but lost to St. Bartholomew's in the second round for the Cup.

For the season 1939–40 Gordon T. E. Jenkins was Captain, but the Inter-Hospitals Cup Competition was cancelled on account of the war, but on March 30, 1940, a seven-a-side tournament was held on the Richmond Athletic Ground. King's was represented by G. T. E. Jenkins (Captain), W. J. Tyson, F. A. Binks, J. J. Y. Dawson, T. G. Filbee, A. W. Kenneth, and W. B. Young. King's drew a bye in the first round, but lost to St. Mary's in the second round by three goals and a try to nothing. St. Mary's won the competition by beating the Middlesex in the final round by 13 points to 3.

For the season 1940–1 A. C. Palmer was re-elected President; F. A. Binks was elected Captain, A. B. Kinnier Wilson, Vice-Captain, and H. McColl, Secretary. James L. Livingstone continued to be Treasurer.

From 1935 to 1941 some of the outstanding members of the Rugby fifteens, apart from those already named were: D. R. Barnes, Roy Dunstan, E. Haigh, J. B. Houghton, H. O. Jones, A. B. Kinnier Wilson, Hugh H. McColl, F. A. Milne, R. A. Palmer, A. F. Wallace, J. W. Warrick, and R. O. Wheeler. During the season 1938–9 W. B. Young, the former Cambridge Blue, played for Scotland, Kent, and the Barbarians, W. J. Tyson played for the East Midlands, and Denis F. Glass played for the United Hospitals.

During the period under consideration the success of the first fifteens was due in great measure to the coaching by the old Internationals R. Cove-Smith, David J. MacMyn, and Alec C. Palmer.

During the period of the war King's played Rugby at Horton, the sports ground at Dog Kennel Hill having been damaged. Play was resumed at the Medical Sports Ground in October 1946. In the first round of the Inter-Hospitals Cup Competition in 1946 King's beat St. George's but lost to Guy's in the second round. In 1947 there was no Inter-Hospitals Cup Competition but matches seven-a-side were arranged. King's played St. Mary's in the second round and lost 5 points to nil. In 1948 the competition was resumed. King's, captained by Colin S. C. Roberts, drew with the Westminster 3 points each, but lost the replay.

During many seasons Alec C. Palmer, the President, took a keen practical interest in the Club; more recently Vernon F. Hall and Denis F. Glass have helped the teams with practical advice.

The Hospitals Rugby Challenge Cup
For King's previous records see *King's*, p. 474.

1935	King's	*v.* The London.	0–0 drawn.
	,,	*v.* The London (replay).	3–0 won.
	,,	*v.* St. Thomas's.	5–0 won.
	,,	*v.* U.C.H.	22–3 won.
	,,	*v.* St. Mary's (the final).	3–11 lost.
1936	,,	*v.* The London.	12–4 won.
	,,	*v.* St. Thomas's.	3–9 lost.
1937	,,	*v.* St. Thomas's.	0–4 lost.
1938	,,	*v.* The London.	19–3 won.
	,,	*v.* Guy's.	0–0 drawn.
	,,	*v.* Guy's (replay).	3–6 lost.
1939	,,	*v.* St. George's.	14–4 won.
	,,	*v.* St. Bartholomew's	0–8 lost.
1946	,,	*v.* St. George's.	5–0 won.
	,,	*v.* Guy's.	0–31 lost.
1948	,,	*v.* The Westminster.	3–3 drawn.
	,,	*v.* The Westminster (replay).	3–10 lost.

THE ASSOCIATION FOOTBALL CLUB

In 1946 the Club was recommenced at King's and officers were elected: John Bell Milne, President; J. R. Franklin, Captain; T. McVey, Treasurer, and T. Lucas, Secretary. Matches were arranged to be played on the Medical School Ground at Dog Kennel Hill.

KING'S COLLEGE HOSPITAL CRICKET CLUB

In the previous volume, *King's and some King's Men*, the names of those in the cricket eleven which won the Inter-Hospitals Cricket

Cup in 1882 and in 1883 are given. The cricket eleven of 1887 consisted of H. J. Scott (a member of the Australian sides which had previously toured England), T. Boswell Beach, T. Grigor Brodie, Harold D. Castle, Charles W. Hopewell, H. McLean, A. R. Savill, Charles T. Standring, Herbert Skipton, W. Doherty Wells, and Charles Williams.

In 1935 the team, captained by John H. Walters, lost to St. Thomas's in the first round of the Inter-Hospitals Cricket Cup, and in 1936 the side, captained by A. D. Hodges, again lost to St. Thomas's in the first round.

In 1937 the team, captained by T. N. G. Copestake, lost to St. Mary's in the first round. In 1938 the side, captained by H. G. Bynoe, and ably supported by D. J. Fairweather, an excellent all-round player, drew a bye in the first round, beat the London in the second round, but lost to St. George's in the semi-final round. In 1939 G. T. E. Jenkins was Captain and John C. Hawks Secretary. The team lost to St. Bartholomew's in the first round of the Inter-Hospitals Cup. The enjoyable match of the season was 'Past (captained by John H. Peel) v. Present', in which the 'Present' team was victorious.

The more prominent members of the teams of 1934–9 were: E. D. Arkell, J. T. Burrowes, H. G. Bynoe, R. W. E. Bynoe, T. N. G. Copestake, D. J. Fairweather, John C. Hawks, A. D. Hodges, G. T. E. Jenkins, D. A. H. Ritchie, W. J. Tyson, B. B. Waddy, L. H. Waddy, J. H. Walters, and J. R. Wilson.

For the season 1940 John C. Hawks was Captain, D. A. H. Ritchie, Vice-Captain, and M. P. Nelson, Secretary.

In 1944 V. H. Wheble was Captain, supported by R. St. J. Buxton, A. L. O. Latta, and K. F. Weeks.

In 1946 K. F. Weeks captained the side; he was ably supported by Ross Stewart. King's lost to Guy's in the first round of the Inter-Hospitals Cup Tie.

THE LAWN TENNIS CLUB

In the previous volume it was stated that the Lawn Tennis Club was inaugurated in the year 1907. Further investigation indicates that there was a Lawn Tennis Six representing King's in 1906. The team then consisted of Harold W. Wiltshire (see *King's*, p. 419), E. W. Matthews, A. Scott Gillett, Douglas Hamilton, John Everidge (see p. 129), and R. B. Roe. This team was narrowly beaten by Guy's at Honor Oak in the Inter-Hospitals Junior Cup Tie in the summer of that year.

In 1913 the team consisted of G. Blogg and L. B. Goldschmidt, A. S. Wakely and H. L. Addison, Hugh A. Richards (Captain) and Kenneth Playfair. For the Junior Inter-Hospitals Cup this team beat the Middlesex Hospital Second VI, University College Hospital VI, and St. Mary's VI, but lost the final tie to the Royal Dental Hospital. For the Cheatle Cup L. B. Goldschmidt beat A. S. Wakely, the holder of the Cup for 1912.

In 1935 the team, captained by G. R. Steed, drew a bye in the first round of the Inter-Hospitals Lawn Tennis Cup Competition, defeated the Middlesex in the second round, but lost to Guy's in the semi-final. The outstanding players for King's were O. Gunnery, G. R. Steed, and D. I. Williams. The Cheatle Cup that year was won by J. D. Moore.

In 1936 T. G. S. James was Captain and D. I. Williams, Secretary. The members of the Second VI were M. L. Corera, B. B. Waddy, A. D. Picton, G. W. Kennedy, R. R. Wethered, and J. W. Warrick. This team reached the final tie by overcoming the London and then the Middlesex, but eventually lost to the Westminster. During the season the Cheatle Cup was won by F. Owen.

In 1937 the team, captained by R. R. Wethered, lost to St. Bart's in the final round of the cup competition. The Cheatle Cup was won by G. R. Steed.

In 1938 the side, captained by J. W. Warrick, lost to the Middlesex in the first round of the cup competition. The Cheatle Cup was won by R. B. Southwell.

In 1939 the 'first six', captained by R. P. Crick, beat the Middlesex in the Cup match 8–5, but in the next round lost to St. Mary's, 5–10.

Since 1929 Victor E. Negus (see p. 129), the President, has been most helpful and encouraging to the members of the Club, and for many years he has captained the 'Past' side against the 'Present' in the annual match.

During more recent years the main supporters of the Lawn Tennis side have been F. Owen, R. P. Crick, J. D. Moore, T. G. S. James, G. R. Steed, J. W. Warrick, and D. I. Williams.

In 1946 the Club was revived after doing little during the period of the war. An American Tournament was held and Victor Negus, the President, presented the prizes.

THE HOCKEY CLUB

In 1907 E. W. Matthews (see p. 12), who was then playing hockey for the United Hospitals and for the Surrey County Eleven, raised the first hockey team at King's to compete in the Inter-Hospitals Hockey Competition. The team included E. Bellis Clayton (see p. 66), A. F. Comyn, H. E. Gibson (see *King's*, p. 349) Arthur D. Griffith (see *King's*, p. 314), and E. W. Matthews (Captain). King's met St. Bartholomew's and lost by 3–0.

In 1913 H. A. Richards was Captain of the team, which included W. S. Birch, H. H. P. Morton, G. T. Symons, H. J. H. Symons, and R. H. Yolland. King's lost to Guy's in the first round of the Inter-Hospitals Cup Competition by 7–1.

In 1935 John H. Walters, an excellent back, was Captain of the side; the other two outstanding members of the team were B. B. Waddy in goal and C. I. Murphie, forward. In the first round of the Inter-Hospitals Cup matches King's drew with Guy's but lost the replay. King's second team lost to the Middlesex.

In 1936 J. Comyn was Captain; he with T. G. S. James and P. H. Jobson played for the United Hospitals. In the first round for the Inter-Hospitals Cup King's lost to the London, and King's second team lost to St. Thomas's.

In 1937 O. Gunnery was Captain of the side and was well supported by J. W. Richmond (Vice-Captain), T. N. G. Copestake, and D. J. Fairweather; King's first team beat U.C.H. and Charing Cross but lost to St. Thomas's; King's second team lost to St. Thomas's. In 1938 P. H. Jobson was Captain and K. Wood, Vice-Captain, supported by D. J. Fairweather and D. A. H. Ritchie. The first team beat Charing Cross but lost to the Westminster. King's second team lost to U.C.H.

During the war period (1939–45) those who helped to keep the club active were John Briggs, K. Carruthers, G. F. Ensor, J. S. Hayward, O. A. N. Husain, J. Merryfield, J. R. Miller, B. Pickles, and V. H. Wheble.

During the season 1945–6 the Inter-Hospitals Cup Competition was resumed, but King's lost to St. Bart's 1–4. For the season 1946–7 Basil Pickles was Captain and R. St. J. Buxton, Vice-Captain; they were well supported by J. Adams, W. H. B. Begg, D. M. Belgrave, O. A. N. Husain, B. W. Mead, Colin S. C. Roberts, J. L. V. Summerhayes, and G. H. Yates. In the first round for the Inter-Hospitals Cup, King's beat the Westminster, but lost to Guy's in the second round. In the United-Hospitals six-a-side tournament, King's reached the final but lost to St. Mary's.

For the season 1947–8 K. F. Weeks was Captain and W. H. B. Begg, Vice-Captain. The latter and R. St. J. Buxton were selected to play in the Surrey County Trial match.

Cup-Tie Results

1935	King's	*v.* Guy's.	Drawn.
	,,	*v.* Guy's (the replay).	Lost.
1936	,,	*v.* The London.	Lost.
1937	,,	*v.* U.C.H.	Won.
	,,	*v.* Charing Cross.	Won.
	,,	*v.* St. Thomas's.	Lost.
1938	,,	*v.* Charing Cross.	Won.
	,,	*v.* Westminster.	Lost.
1939	,,	*v.* London.	Lost.
1946	,,	*v.* St. Bartholomew's	Lost.
1947	,,	*v.* Westminster.	Won.
	,,	*v.* Guy's.	Lost.

THE WOMEN'S HOCKEY CLUB

The Women's Hockey Club was founded in 1921, chiefly by the efforts of Christine P. Francis and Katharine M. Andrew. The first President was H. A. Thomas Fairbank (see p. 116). In 1922 the side was captained by N. B. Daniel, while Winifred P. Edmunds acted as Secretary. In 1923 Freda K. Herbert was Captain, but at the end of the season 1924 the club came to an end, chiefly because of the difficulty in finding a suitable ground. In 1927 the club was restarted, a pitch having been secured in North Ealing; Lilian M. J. Henry was Captain. In 1928 Keren I. Parkes was Captain and Gwendoline E. Austin, Secretary. In the following year 1929 G. E. Austin was Captain and Irene P. Murray, Secretary, but after the spring of 1930 the club failed to survive.

THE MEDICAL SCHOOL GOLFING SOCIETY

In 1912, owing to the enthusiasm of T. P. Legg, the first golf match took place at West Drayton between teams representing the honorary staff and the students, captained by H. A. Richards; the students won.

In the following year the match again took place at West Drayton; this time the staff proved successful. On this occasion the teams were:

Staff: Charlton Briscoe, Arthur H. Cheatle, G. Lenthal Cheatle, Charles W. M. Hope, T. P. Legg, Arthur Whitfield, Harold W. Wiltshire, P. B. Ridge, with Stephen Mayou and W. Stewart.

Students: E. W. Carrington, W. H. W. Cheyne, John Everidge, Eric G. Gauntlett, A. E. Grevell, R. H. Leigh, A. C. McAlister, Gilbert Moore, V. E. Negus, and H. A. Richards.

The present Medical School Golfing Society was inaugurated in 1926, when John Everidge and James L. Livingstone arranged with the Addington Golf Club that members of the Medical School might play there during week-day afternoons at a reduced rate.

Members of the Medical School Golfing Society conform to the regulations of the Addington Golf Club which possesses one of the best courses near London.

The officers of K.C.H. Club are a President, Vice-President, Honorary Secretary, and three members of the Committee, one of whom is a member of the honorary medical staff, one a student working in the Medical School of the Hospital, and one a student of King's working in the Medical Faculty of King's College, London. On November 19, 1926, the Society became incorporated in the Clubs' and Societies' Union.

The first President was John Everidge, the first Vice-President, William Gilliatt, and first Honorary Secretary, David J. MacMyn.

The Annual Match 'Staff v. Students' takes place in the spring and usually ends in a victory for the honorary staff, but in 1938 the students proved successful.

In 1933 John B. Hunter was elected President; he presented two cups to the Society which are played for annually in open foursome competition.

In 1937 F. G. Ethiraj was elected Captain.

The first round of the Inter-Hospitals Golf Cup, 1938–9, was played against the Westminster Hospital at Addington in September 1938; King's lost.

THE INTER-HOSPITALS BOAT RACE: THE ROWING CLUB

In 1935 C. W. A. Searle won the Senior Inter-Hospitals Sculls for the third time in succession.

During the summer the King's crew, consisting of O. Gunnery (cox), George H. H. Dunkerton, Philip W. Edmondson, A. P. Kitchin, and T. C. Probyn, rowed in the 'Rugger Fours' in the United Hospitals' Regatta. King's finished fourth.

THE SAILING CLUB

Mainly through the efforts of H. K. Graham Hodgson, who at the time was Director of the Radiological Department, the Sailing Club was established in 1930. Graham Hodgson became the first President and Hugh W. Davies the Honorary Secretary. Through the

President's influence a dinghy was provided for practice on the Thames.

In 1935 John B. Hunter was elected President, B. S. Illoway became Honorary Secretary, and P. W. Edmondson, Boatswain.

In 1937 D. H. Davies was elected Secretary. In May 1938 twelve members and guests attended the King's Annual Regatta at Burnham.

The winners of the tankards were: J. W. Warrick (crewed by W. J. Tyson), 1; D. J. Fairweather (crewed by K. Wood), 2.

In 1939 the Medical School Regatta was held in July; C. G. R. Sell and H. McColl obtained first place, P. Farr and G. F. W. Tripp second place, and J. W. Warrick with W. J. Tyson third place.

In 1947 the club was re-formed under the Presidency of Hugh W. Davis, Honorary Radiologist at King's. The boat house chosen was at Surbiton and the first Commodore was R. Saxon Snell. In 1948 Terence East (see p. 151) became President and Dorothy J. Webber was Commodore. The Treasurer and Secretary for 1947 and 1948 was G. R. Hervey.

THE SWIMMING CLUB

The club was inaugurated in May 1921. The first President was H. A. Thomas Fairbank and the first Secretary was A. C. Sommerville. Great interest in the club was taken by Thomas Fairbank (see p. 116); he remained President for many years and instituted the Fairbank Challenge Cup for maximum points in men's events. He was followed in office by John B. Hunter, who was President for five years; he was succeeded by John Everidge and he by R. D. Lawrence.

The club usually met on Tuesday evenings at the Camberwell Baths. During each season water polo matches were played and the Inter-Hospitals Water Polo Cup Competition entered, but so far it has not been won by King's.

The Annual Swimming Gala usually took place in October, either at the Bath Club or at the Royal Automobile Club Baths.

In 1934 the annual Swimming Gala was held at the R.A.C. Baths, the Captain was A. D. Picton and he won the Fairbank Cup. In 1935 A. D. Picton again won the Fairbank Cup. In 1936 and 1937 the Fairbank Cup was won by F. E. Stock; in the latter year he also won the Briscoe Cup, for the winner of men's 100 yards free style, and the Everidge Cup for men's one-length free style, but A. D. Picton was outstanding for magnificent diving. In 1938 R. M. Lattey was Captain of the club; the three cups were again won by F. E. Stock, but in each case J. B. Houghton was runner-up.

Apart from those already named the following have been active members of the club since its inauguration: E. N. Butler, M. L. Bynoe, Terence C. Cawthorne (see p. 114), R. Cove-Smith (see p. 93), A. W. Cubitt, R. D. Gawler, R. J. Gilpin, W. M. Gray, A. S. Hollins, E. I. Jones, C. R. Lane, C. R. L'E. Orme, N. C. Parfit, H. L. Rayner, H. H. Renyard, D. A. H. Ritchie, and E. J. Somerset (see p. 100), and also Monica Austin, Islay C. Barne, Olive K. Tubby, and Celia K. Westropp.

Winners of the Fairbank Challenge Cup

1927 H. N. Knox
1929 W. N. P. Wakeley
1933 C. W. J. Claydon
1934 and 1935 A. D. Picton
1936, 1937, and 1938 F. E. Stock

THE SQUASH COURTS

Upon the initiative of Harry A. Lucas, Assistant Pathologist (see p. 136), a committee, on which Mr. I. J. Pitman represented the Committee of Management, was formed in order to consider ways and means of building Squash Racquets Courts. The sum of £600 was granted anonymously by members of the Committee of Management upon the understanding that when the money was paid back it should be put to the funds of the Hospital. Some members of the honorary staff of King's promised a similar amount of money in the form of nominal debentures. The undertaking was also supported financially by the *K.C.H. Gazette*.

Building of two Squash Courts commenced in 1932 and they were opened for play in 1933.

The foundation money was paid off and the Clubs' and Societies' Union then took over the control of the courts.

THE SQUASH CLUB

In 1937 John Everidge was elected President of the club, R. R. Wethered became Captain, and T. G. N. Copestake, Secretary.

The 'John Everidge' Cup was won by T. G. N. Copestake after a close match in the final with D. J. Fairweather.

THE MEDICAL SCHOOL DANCE CLUB

The Dance Club was inaugurated in 1921. The President is chosen from the members of the honorary medical staff and the Secretary is usually one of the senior students of the Medical School.

The club dances were formerly held in the Library of the Medical School, but in recent years in the Medical School refectory hall. On many occasions the Dental Dance Band has supplied the music.

The Annual Club Dance is held in the West End usually in November or December. The dances are invariably a financial success: on one occasion the club was able to hand over the sum of £56 to the Medical School Building Fund, and on many occasions it has been able to augment the funds of the Clubs' and Societies' Union.

Some years before the Dance Club was inaugurated an Annual Hospital Dance was held and well attended by both staff and students. From the proceeds of the Hospital Dance held at the Wharncliffe Rooms in 1913 the Clubs' and Societies' Union benefited by the sum of £25.

KING'S COLLEGE HOSPITAL GAZETTE
Founded 1913, Re-established 1922

'A Gazette chiefly for the students, partly of the students, and entirely by the students: that freedom may not perish from the earth.'

So runs the epigram on the cover of Vol. 20, No. 1, January number of the *Gazette*, 1941.

From 1935 to 1948 the *Gazette* has appeared regularly, even during the period of the war. The Committee has been ably assisted by St. John D. Buxton, Chairman from 1929 until 1946 when he retired, to be succeeded by F. F. Cartwright the present Chairman.

During recent years the *Gazette* has published some excellent portraits: Charlton Briscoe (Oct. 1935), H. A. Thomas Fairbank (Apr. 1936), S. A. Kinnier Wilson (July 1937), Miss M. A. Willcox (Oct. 1937), John Thomson-Walker (Jan. 1938), J. A. Drake with M. Sydney Thomson (Apr. 1938), A Laryngological Group—Greville Macdonald, St. Clair Thomson, and Charles W. M. Hope (Apr. 1941), and G. Frederic Still (Aug. 1941). There are three pictures of groups (July 1938) in which Charles E. Newman, now Dean of the British Postgraduate Medical School, appears; in that of 1922 he is seen with a group of students, the members of the staff present being Harold Wiltshire and Douglas Firth; in the groups of 1932 and 1933 he is there as a member of the honorary medical staff with his colleagues Douglas Firth and Terence East.

In the April number of 1940 there are photographic reproductions of some outstanding students: G. T. E. Jenkins, L. D. de Launay, W. E. Alderson, John Hawks, Roy Dunstan, and Beth Waller.

There are also interesting pictures of the Rugby Football teams:

that in the April number for 1935 represents the finalists in the Inter-Hospitals Cup, with J. D. Moore, Captain. The team of 1935–6 appears in the April number 1936 and that for 1936–7 in the April number of 1937 with A. C. Palmer, President. The team for 1938–9 appears in the January number for 1939, also with A. C. Palmer, President. The Hockey team for 1935–6 appears in the April number for 1936 with St. John D. Buxton as President of the Club.

Editors of the Gazette

1935	D. G. Allen	1943	Norman S. Hooton
1936	C. A. Gibson-Hill	1943	J. P. D. Mounsey
1937	D. I. Williams	1944	Bevis H. Brock
1938	A. H. Baynes	1944	H. F. Barnes
1939	S. F. Taylor	1945	J. Towers
1940	W. E. Alderson	1946	A. John Kenny
1941	J. V. Morris	1947	Colin Roberts
1941	E. James Anthony	1948	A. A. Hobbs
1942	John H. Cule.	1948	W. H. B. Begg

APPENDIX
1935–1948

SECTION XIII

THE MEDICAL FELLOWS OF KING'S COLLEGE, LONDON.
THE MEDICAL ASSOCIATES OF KING'S COLLEGE, LONDON.
THE SCHOLARS, EXHIBITIONERS, MEDALLISTS, AND
SPECIAL PRIZE WINNERS OF KING'S COLLEGE
HOSPITAL MEDICAL SCHOOL

(For previous lists, see *King's*, pp. 509–40)

THE NAMES OF MEDICAL FELLOWS OF KING'S COLLEGE, LONDON, ELECTED SINCE 1934

1939 *Lionel Vernon Cargill, F.R.C.S., Consulting Ophthalmic Surgeon to K.C.H.

1945 *Victor Ewings Negus, M.S., F.R.C.S., Senior Surgeon for Diseases of the Ear, Nose, and Throat, K.C.H.

Robert John Stewart McDowall, M.D., D.Sc., F.R.C.P. (Ed.), Professor of Physiology, K.C.L.

1948 *Hugh Alexander Dunlop, M.Sc., M.D., F.R.C.P., Physician to Charing Cross Hospital.

1949 *James Livingstone Livingstone, M.D., F.R.C.P., Physician to K.C.H.

MEDICAL ASSOCIATES OF KING'S COLLEGE, LONDON, APPOINTED AFTER 1934

1945 Briggs, Edmund James Seeds Nixon.

1947 Brown, John Alexander Hunter.

1941 †Cumings, Christopher Felis.

1940 †Cutting, Alfred Howard.

1945 †Douglas, Joy Marjorie.

1944 †Doust, John William Lovett.

1945 †Harding, Kathleen Mary.

1939 †Hobbs, Frank Edward.

1944 Howells, John Gwilym.

1943 Lewis, Arthur Picton Rossiter.

1942 †Mason, Stanley Arthur.

1946 Philip, Peter Forbes.

1940 Rowan, Robert William.

1939 †Russell, Arthur Frederick.

1938 †Stock, Francis Edgar.

1945 †Toye, Donald Kenneth Morley.

1947 Walkey, Gilbert Benjamin Rowland.

1938 †Warner, Kenneth Orme.

1938 Watts, Arthur Stanley.

1935 †Whittles, James Hill.

SENIOR SCHOLARS IN THE MEDICAL SCHOOL

1935 J. V. Dacie.

1936 A. J. Heriot.

H. F. West.

1937 A. J. Heriot.

1938 E. Cronin.

1939 S. Oram.

1940 R. A. Sandison.

1941 R. A. Moir.

* Indicates a former student in the Medical Faculty of King's College, London.
† Members of King's College Hospital Medical School.

SENIOR SCHOLARS IN THE MEDICAL SCHOOL *(continued)*

1942 B. S. Cardell.
1943 T. Hanley.
1944 V. H. Wheble.
1945 T. A. Richards.

1946 Alice M. Sibly.
1947 B. W. Meade.
1948 Brenda M. Davies.

JELF MEDALLISTS

1935 D. G. Allen.
1936 J. Smallpeice.
     G. T. Stockings.
1937 H. W. C. Fuller.
1938 F. E. Stock.
1939 A. F. Russell.
     P. D. Samman.
1940 H. H. Renyard.

1942 B. S. Lush.
1943 J. R. Briggs.
     R. J. Bush.
1944 N. S. Hooton.
1945 Joy Marjorie Douglas.
1946 L. Silverstone.
1947 J. L. Gowans.
1948 L. R. Davis.

TODD PRIZE AND MEDAL FOR CLINICAL MEDICINE

1935 J. V. Dacie.
1936 Eileen P. Gretton-Watson.
1937 A. J. Heriot.
1938 F. E. Stock.
1939 A. F. Russell.
1940 Mary E. Eiloart.
1941 R. A. Moir.

1942 B. S. Cardell.
1943 J. P. Hopewell.
1944 J. P. D. Mounsey.
1945 J. B. Metcalfe.
1947 J. L. Gowans.
     B. W. Mead.
1948 Brenda M. Davies.

TODD PRIZE (SECOND) FOR CLINICAL MEDICINE

1935 G. T. Stockings.
1937 H. W. C. Fuller.
1938 P. H. Jobson.
1939 J. M. Naish.
1940 R. A. Sandison.
1942 S. G. Tuffill.

1943 T. Hanley.
     R. J. Bush.
1944 Alison Benson Dunbar.
1945 T. A. Richards.
1948 L. R. Davis.
     D. C. Lindley.

TANNER PRIZE FOR OBSTETRICS

1935 S. O. Aylett.
1936 H. F. West.
     Mary J. Allardice.
1937 H. W. C. Fuller.
1938 J. Todd.
1939 R. H. Elphinstone.
1940 M. Elias.
1941 R. A. Moir.

1942 R. A. Palmer.
     S. G. Tuffill.
1943 E. L. Trickey.
1944 Kathleen L. Prendergast.
1945 T. A. Richards.
1947 B. W. Meade.
1948 J. D. Arneaud.
     K. G. Prior.

BURRIDGE PRIZE FOR FORENSIC MEDICINE

1935 J. Smallpeice.
1936 A. J. Heriot.
1937 R. B. Niven.

1938 E. Cronin.
1939 S. Oram.
1940 R. A. Sandison.

BURRIDGE PRIZE FOR FORENSIC MEDICINE *(continued)*

1941 R. A. Moir.
1942 B. S. Cardell.
1943 W. E. J. Bennett.
1944 Catherine E. Crane.

1945 L. Silverstone.
1946 D. J. Chapman.
1947 L. Kader.
1948 J. D. Arneaud.

JOCELYN ALMOND PRIZE FOR DISEASES OF CHILDREN

1935 J. V. Dacie.
1936 A. Nimalasuria.
1937 H. W. C. Fuller.
1938 Nora Reid.
1939 A. F. Russell.
1940 Jean D. McKendrick.
1941 Joan Cleland.

1942 Rosemary I. Cook.
1943 Norah C. Elphinstone.
1944 V. H. Wheble.
1945 Irene M. S. Chappel.
1946 H. G. Mather.
1947 O. A. N. Husain.
1948 Margaret H. Jerwood.

FERRIER PRIZE IN NEUROLOGY

1944 A. B. Kinnier Wilson.

LEGG PRIZE FOR SURGERY

1935 S. J. Stein.
1936 A. J. Heriot.
1937 G. H. H. Dunkerton.
      H. W. C. Fuller.
1938 E. Cronin.
1939 R. G. Evans.
1940 H. H. Renyard.
1941 C. G. R. Sell.

1942 J. W. L. Doust.
1943 P. H. Huggill.
1944 N. S. Hooton.
1945 W. Waugh.
1946 Alice Mary Sibly.
1947 Iris Kane.
1948 S. J. Beales.

LEGG PRIZE FOR SURGICAL PATHOLOGY

1935 S. O. Aylett.
1936 A. Nimalasuria.
1937 H. W. C. Fuller.
1938 Edith A. M. Whetnall.
1939 E. B. Wild.
1940 J. P. Childs.
1941 Joan Cleland.

1942 D. R. Barnes.
      S. G. Tuffill.
1943 T. Hanley.
1944 V. H. Wheble.
1945 Mary H. Moller.
1946 L. T. Cotton.
1947 R. C. Read.
1948 J. D. Arneaud.

CHEYNE PRIZE FOR SURGERY

1935 D. G. Allen.
1936 H. F. West.
1937 A. J. Heriot.
1938 P. H. Jobson.
1939 A. F. Russell.
1940 R. A. Sandison.
1941 R. A. Moir.
1942 B. S. Cardell.

1943 T. Hanley.
      J. R. Briggs.
1944 B. C. Smith.
1945 Mary H. Moller.
1946 L. Silverstone.
1947 A. J. Kenny.
      R. C. Read.
1948 Elizabeth G. S. McDowall.

WARE PRIZE FOR GENERAL PATHOLOGY

1935 A. H. Baynes.
     A. H. Cutting.
1936 P. D. Samman.
1937 Jean D. McKendrick.
1938 G. W. D. Henderson.
1939 J. A. Ainslie.

1940 R. B. Coles.
1945 Elizabeth Bennett.
1946 J. M. Hinton.
1947 Muriel P. Reynolds.
1948 J. Terry.

C. E. WALLIS PRIZE

1934 R. W. Lovel.
1936 A. J. Sheldon.
1938 C. M. Johnston.
1940 J. B. Bell.
     C. H. Vigar.

1943 R. A. Cawson.
1944 A. C. L. Stubbings.
1946 R. J. Sharland.

PROFESSOR ERNEST WHITE PRIZE FOR PSYCHOLOGICAL MEDICINE

1939 K. F. Wilsdon.
1941 J. W. L. Doust.

1943 T. Hanley.
1948 E. T. Thomas.

SIR WILLIAM SIMPSON PRIZE FOR TROPICAL MEDICINE

1941 F. E. Hobbs.
1942 Edith Margaret M. Toye
1944 P. T. Clover.

1945 S. R. Shaw.
1948 J. F. T. Allison.

WILLIAM BLAIR-BELL PRIZE IN GYNAECOLOGY

1948 G. A. Gresham.
     J. M. Brudenell (*proxime accessit*).

SPECIAL PRIZE FOR DISEASES OF THE SKIN

1939 Mary Elizabeth Eiloart.

SPECIAL PRIZE FOR ORTHOPAEDIC SURGERY

1939 A. F. Wallace.

SPECIAL PRIZE FOR UROLOGY

1939 W. M. Stephens.

MEDICAL ENTRANCE SCHOLARSHIPS (SCIENCE)

1935 T. H. E. Richards.
1936 R. A. Moir.
1937 R. J. Bush.
1938 J. E. L. Price.
1939 G. Grant.
1940 T. A. Richards.

1941 P. C. Harris.
1942 J. L. Gowans.
1943 J. K. Carter.
1946 R. E. H. Partridge.
1947 T. Hargreaves.
1948 A. R. Barber.

MEDICAL ENTRANCE SCHOLARSHIPS
(ANATOMY AND PHYSIOLOGY)

1935 N. L. Crabtree (Lond.).
    B. H. Price (Cantab.).
1936 R. H. Elphinstone (Cantab.).
1937 D. A. Barley (Lond.).
1938 H. O. Jones (Lond.).
1939 S. G. Tuffill (Lond.).
1940 J. Attenborough (Cantab.).
1941 J. R. M. Miller (Lond.).

1942 W. Waugh (Cantab.).
1943 Iris Kane (Cantab.).
1944 Joan D. M. Baker (Lond.).
    O. A. N. Husain (Lond.).
1946 P. E. B. Holmes (Lond.).
1947 Francis E. Mather (Lond.).
1948 B. H. Kelham (Cantab.).

MEDICAL ENTRANCE SCHOLARSHIPS IN
GENERAL PATHOLOGY

1937 R. J. R. Cureton (Cantab.).
1941 V. H. Wheble (Oxon.).
1942 Edith M. Davies (Cantab.).
    Margaret H. Jordan (Cantab.).

1944 P. H. A. Sneath (Exhibition)
    (Cantab.).
1946 Dinah D. Webb (Cantab.).
1947 M. G. Rinsler (Exhibition)
    (Cantab.).

EPSOM COLLEGE SCHOLARSHIPS

1935 J. M. Watson (Cantab.).
1936 J. C. Hawks (Oxon.).
1940 C. H. R. Knowles (Lond.).
1944 N. Lees (Lond.).

1945 A. A. Hobbs (Lond.).
1946 J. R. Edsall (Cantab.).
1947 M. K. Mason (Lond.).

THE 'BURNEY YEO' BEQUEST SCHOLARSHIPS
Scholars

1935 A. H. Baynes (Cantab.).
1936 J. T. Burrowes (Oxon.).
    S. F. Taylor (Oxon.).
1937 W. E. Alderson (Oxon.).
    W. J. Tyson (Oxon.).
1938 J. P. Childs (Oxon.).
    D. Micklewright (Oxon.).
1942 B. H. Brock (Cantab.).
    E. L. N. Shoeten-Sack (Oxon.).
1943 H. G. Mather (Cantab.).
    A. V. Adams (Cantab.).

1943 J. Towers (Oxon.).
1944 R. C. Read (Cantab.).
    G. W. C. Johnson (Cantab.).
    N. Tate (Cantab.).
1945 G. R. Hervey (Cantab.).
1946 G. A. Gresham (Cantab.).
    A. G. Ackerley (Cantab.).
1947 C. R. Leeson (Cantab.).
    T. S. Leeson (Cantab.).
1948 H. Sunderland (Cantab.).

Exhibitioners

1935 R. R. Wethered (Oxon.).
1936 J. M. Naish (Cantab.).
1937 C. C. Evans (Cantab.).

1938 R. V. Young (Oxon.).
    H. McColl (Cantab.).
    W. W. Brigden (Cantab.).
1946 J. H. Wakely (Oxon.).

THE RAYMOND GOOCH SCHOLARSHIPS

Scholars

1935 E. Cronin (Cantab.).	1943 I. S. M. Jones (Cantab.).
1936 P. D. Samman (Cantab.).	1944 C. S. C. Roberts (Cantab.).
1937 G. T. E. Jenkins (Lond.).	K. J. M. Carruthers (Lond.).
1938 C. G. R. Sell (Cantab.).	

Exhibitioners

1935 J. H. Whittles (Lond.).	1938 F. S. Strong (Lond.).
1936 R. M. Lattey (Oxon.).	W. B. Young (Cantab.).
S. Oram (Lond.).	1942 P. G. Laing (Lond.).
1937 D. G. C. Macdonald (Lond.).	1943 K. A. Sowden (Lond.).
K. F. Wilsdon (Oxon.).	1945 D. B. J. Wardle (Cantab.).
1938 J. R. G. Edwards (Lond.).	Joy Kathleen Goodacre
S. A. Mason (Lond.).	(Cantab.).

SEAMAN SCHOLARSHIPS

1936 J. J. Y. Dawson.	1940 A. B. Philip.
1937 H. R. E. Wallis.	1942 C. W. Shaw.
1938 F. P. Morris.	

ENTRANCE SCHOLARSHIPS, EXHIBITIONS, AND PRIZES AT KING'S COLLEGE, LONDON, OBTAINED BY STUDENTS OF KING'S COLLEGE HOSPITAL MEDICAL SCHOOL

The awards are by King's College, University of London.

WARNEFORD SCHOLARSHIPS

1935 Winifrid M. Bond.	1939 J. A. Hanraty.
Jean D. McKendrick.	A. L. O. Latta.
V. H. Springett.	1940 Joy M. Douglas.
1936 H. O. Jones.	D. K. M. Toye.
1937 V. Blackman.	1941 J. K. Baird.
E. Haigh.	1942 S. J. Beales.
A. Stoddart.	C. H. Neaves.
1938 Rosemary I. Cook.	1945 Sheila C. S. Meux.
C. D. T. James.	1946 Avisa J. M. Morley.
R. G. Davies.	

SAMBROOKE EXHIBITIONS IN MEDICAL SCIENCE

1935 H. H. Renyard.	1941 Joan D. M. Baker.
1936 F. A. Binks.	K. B. Roberts.
1937 B. S. Cardell.	1942 A. J. Kenny.
1939 R. L. M. Ferrari.	1943 N. D. Gower.
1940 P. T. Clover.	1946 J. P. H. Davies.
C. R. B. Vincent.	1947 J. J. Jones.

RABBETH SCHOLARSHIPS

1935 Jean D. McKendrick.
     Winifrid M. Bond.
     Mary P. Parish.
1937 A. Stoddard.
1938 Jean V. Simpson.
     R. G. Davies.

1939 Kathleen A. D. Drury.
1940 R. P. Hickey.
     P. F. Philip.
1941 Janet G. S. McDowall.
     Jean Nicol.
1947 M. E. A. Powell.

LEATHES PRIZE

1936 A. F. Russell.
     A. H. Cutting.
1937 G. W. D. Henderson.
1938 K. O. Warner.

1939 J. W. L. Doust.
1948 Elizabeth Bennett.
     K. J. M. Carruthers.

WARNEFORD PRIZE

1936 Kathleen M. Harding.

1939 F. E. Hobbs.

BARRY PRIZE

1936 Jean D. McKendrick.
1937 G. W. D. Henderson.
1938 K. O. Warner.

1939 H. M. T. Coles.
     Mary Pringle.

ALFRED HUGHES MEMORIAL PRIZE (ANATOMY)

1938 H. O. Jones.
     R. A. Moir.
1940 D. D. C. Howat.
     R. J. Bush.

1944 G. J. Beales.

HUXLEY PRIZE IN PHYSIOLOGY

1936 L. G. White.
1937 Jean D. McKendrick.
1938 H. O. Jones.
1939 V. Blackman.

1940 D. A. Stanley.
1943 J. L. Gowans.
1944 Elizabeth Bennett.

JELF MEDALLISTS AT KING'S COLLEGE, LONDON

1936 A. F. Russell.
1940 R. B. Coles.

1944 J. D. Arneaud.

SECTION XIV

DISTINCTIONS IN THE FACULTY OF MEDICINE IN
THE UNIVERSITY OF LONDON, AT THE ROYAL COLLEGE
OF PHYSICIANS OF LONDON, AT THE ROYAL
COLLEGE OF SURGEONS OF ENGLAND, AND AT THE
SOCIETY OF APOTHECARIES

(For previous lists, see *King's*, pp. 541–7)

THE UNIVERSITY OF LONDON

The following members of the staff of King's College Hospital Medical School were appointed to Professorships in the University:

1937 Edward Mapother, M.D., F.R.C.P., F.R.C.S., Professor of Psychiatry.
1939 Samuel Nevin, B.Sc., M.D., M.R.C.P., Professor of Mental Pathology.
1948 Henry A. Magnus, M.D., Professor of Pathology.
1948 Charles H. Gray, M.Sc., M.B., B.S., Professor of Chemical Pathology.

Honours at the Degree of Doctor of Medicine

1936 Alexander Charles Dalzell (University Medal).
1941 Samuel Oram (University Medal).

Honours at the Degree of M.B., B.S.

1935 Stanley Osborn Aylett (Medicine).
1936 Joyce Mary George (Obstetrics and Gynaecology).
1937 Harold William Charles Fuller (Medicine, Pathology, and Surgery—University Medal).
1937 Alexander John Heriot (Pathology).
1941 Hugh Owen Jones (Surgery).
1941 Raymond Andrew Moir (Medicine, Hygiene and Forensic Medicine).
1942 Sidney George Tuffill (Hygiene, and Forensic Medicine).
1943 Sydney Douglas Gun-Munro (Surgery).
1947 James Learmonth Gowans (Medicine and Pathology.)
Joan Daphne Meskell Baker (Surgery).

Honours at the Degree of Bachelor of Dental Surgery

1936 James Liddell Rossini (Pathology and Bacteriology).
1938 Colin Sidney Syms (Pathology and Bacteriology).
1944 Roderick Anthony Cawson (Pharmacology).
1947 Roy John Sharland (Surgery, Pathology, Bacteriology, Pharmacology, and Orthodontics).
John Antony Crease (Surgery, Pathology, and Bacteriology).

THE ROYAL COLLEGE OF PHYSICIANS OF LONDON
(Incorporated 1518)

(For previous lists see *King's*, pp. 548–51)

Censors

Sir John Charlton Briscoe, Bt., 1930, 1931, 1933.
Arthur Charles Douglas Firth, 1940, 1941, 1944.

Registrar

Sir Raymond H. P. Crawfurd, M.D. Oxon., 1925–38.

Assistant Registrar

Charles E. Newman, M.D. Cantab., 1932–8.

Goulstonian Lecturer

1936 Dr. R. A. McCance.

Croonian Lecturer

1945 Dr. Macdonald Critchley.

Bradshaw Lecturers

1936 Dr. Edward Mapother.
1942 Dr. Macdonald Critchley.

Oliver-Sharpey Lecturer

1946 Dr. R. D. Lawrence.

Weber-Parkes Prize and Medal

1936 Sir St. Clair Thomson for his work on Tuberculosis of the Larynx.

THE ROYAL COLLEGE OF SURGEONS OF ENGLAND
(Charter 1843)

(For previous lists see *King's*, pp. 551–3)

President

1949 Sir Cecil P. G. Wakeley

Member of the Council

1937 Cecil P. G. Wakeley.

Hunterian Professors

1935 Macdonald Critchley.
1937, 1940, 1942 Cecil P. G. Wakeley.
1939 John Henry Mulvany.
1942 Francis Wilfrid Willway.
1943 Lewis Herbert Savin.
1944 St. John Dudley Buxton.
1949 Terence Edward Cawthorne.

Erasmus Wilson Lecturer

1935 Cecil P. G. Wakeley.
1941–4 Cecil P. G. Wakeley.

Bradshaw Lecturer

1947 Cecil P. G. Wakeley.

Robert Jones Lecturer

1938 Harold Arthur Thomas Fairbank.

Hallett Prize

1934 Ananda Nimalasuria.

THE SOCIETY OF APOTHECARIES
(Charter 1617)

Master

1939 Lionel Vernon Cargill.

SECTION XV

NAMES OF SOME OF THE PAST AND PRESENT OFFICERS OF THE KING'S COLLEGE HOSPITAL

PRESIDENTS OF KING'S COLLEGE HOSPITAL

1839–51	The Duke of Sutherland.
1851–7	The Earl of Ellesmere.
1857–1904	The Duke of Cambridge.
1904–35	The Duke of Connaught.
1935–6	The Duke of York.
1937	The Duchess of Gloucester.

CHAIRMEN

(For previous lists, see *King's*, pp. 579–80)

1933–6   The Rt. Hon. Earl Beatty, P.C., G.C.B., O.M.
1936–48 Viscount Hambleden (Third Viscount).
1948   The Marquess of Normanby, M.B.E.

TREASURERS

1921–37 Claud P. Serocold, O.B.E.
1937   R. A. Hornby.

DEPUTY-TREASURERS

1934–5   Sir Basil Blackett, K.C.B., K.C.S.I.
1935–41 Hon. George Colville, M.B.E.
1941–4   C. E. A. Bedwell.

VICE-CHAIRMEN

1934–37 G. L. Hawker.
1937–41 The Hon. George Colville, M.B.E.
1941–5   His Honour Judge Sturges, K.C.
1945–8   William Gilliatt, C.V.O., M.D., M.S., F.R.C.S.

CHAPLAINS

1932–7   The Right Rev. Richard Parsons, Lord Bishop of Southwark.
1937   Rev. Cyril Eastaugh, M.A.

HOUSE GOVERNORS AND SECRETARIES

C. E. A. Bedwell, 1922 to July 1939.
S. W. Barnes, appointed in June 1939.

SECTION XVI

NAMES OF THE OFFICERS OF THE MEDICAL SCHOOL, OF THE INAUGURAL LECTURERS, AND OF THE CHAIRMEN OF THE PAST AND PRESENT STUDENTS' DINNERS

OFFICERS OF KING'S COLLEGE HOSPITAL MEDICAL SCHOOL

(For previous lists see *King's*, p. 564)

DEANS

1932 John Alexander Drake, M.D., F.R.C.P., D.P.H.
1938 John B. Hunter, M.C., M.A., M.Ch., F.R.C.S.
1946 Terence E. Cawthorne, F.R.C.S.
1948 Harold C. Edwards, C.B.E., M.S., F.R.C.S.

VICE-DEANS

1932 H. Audley Lucas, B.A., M.R.C.S., L.R.C.P.
1937 Charles E. Newman, B.A., M.D., F.R.C.P.
1938 A. Wallis Kendall, M.S., F.R.C.S.
1946 Vernon F. Hall, M.R.C.S., L.R.C.P., F.F.A., R.C.S.

DEPUTY VICE-DEAN

1939–46 Terence E. Cawthorne, F.R.C.S.

SECRETARIES

1915 Sidney C. Ranner, M.A. Cantab.
1947 Walter Frank Gunn, LL.B. Lond., F.C.I.S.

CLERK TO THE MEDICAL SCHOOL

1935 Stanley John Balaam.

LIBRARIAN

1946 Mrs. Lilian Sargeant, F.L.A.

ACCOUNTANT

1946 C. H. Meredith, A.C.I.S., A.L.A.A.

INAUGURAL LECTURES DELIVERED IN OCTOBER AT THE COMMENCEMENT OF THE SESSION OF THE MEDICAL SCHOOL

LECTURERS

(See King's, p. 578).

1935 Professor (later Sir) G. Frederic Still, M.D., LL.D., F.R.C.P.

1936 Professor John Beattie, M.D., D.Sc.

1937 Sir (later Lord) Alfred Webb-Johnson, C.B.E., D.S.O., F.R.C.S.

1938 Mr. (later Sir) E. Rock Carling, M.B., B.S., F.R.C.S.

*1947 Sir Edward Mellanby, K.C.B., M.D., F.R.C.P., F.R.S.

*1948 Professor (later Sir) Henry Cohen, M.D., F.R.C.P., F.F.R.

CHAIRMEN OF THE PAST AND PRESENT STUDENTS' ANNUAL DINNERS

(*Usually held in October*)

(See King's, p. 581).

1935 J. Charlton Briscoe.

1936 H. A. Thomas Fairbank.

1937 John A. Drake.

1938 Cuthbert Sprawson.

1947 John B. Hunter (held in February).

1947 William Gilliatt.

1948 John Everidge.

* Formal openings.

SECTION XVII

BENEFACTORS OF AND BENEFACTIONS TO THE MEDICAL DEPARTMENT OF KING'S COLLEGE AND TO KING'S COLLEGE HOSPITAL MEDICAL SCHOOL

1834. Lieut.-General Sir Henry Worsley, G.C.B., the sum of £2,000 as an Endowment for the Education of Medical Missionaries for the British Possessions in India.

1834. Stanley Hammersley Leathes, the sum of £300 Reduced Three per cent. Stock (Reduced Annuities) as an Endowment for Divinity Prizes.

1835. The Reverend Samuel Wilson Warneford, LL.D., the sum of £1,000 as an Endowment for Annual Prizes, and in 1851 the sum of £5,000 as an Endowment of Scholarships in the Medical Department.

1863. The Friends of Robert Bentley Todd, M.D., F.R.S., F.K.C., the sum of £153 as an Endowment Fund for an Annual Bronze Medal and Prize of Books, in memory of his long and distinguished services to King's College Hospital.

1867. Thomas Godfrey Sambrooke, the sum of £2,000 for the purpose of founding a Medical and a Surgical Registrarship, to be attached to King's College and to King's College Hospital, and in 1871, £10,000 Stock for the purpose of founding scholarships and exhibitions.

1868. The Friends of the Reverend Richard William Jelf, D.D., Principal of King's College, London (1844–68), the sum of £225, as an Endowment Fund for a Bronze Medal, to be given annually in each department of King's College and School, in memory of his long connexion with the College.

1872. The Friends of Thomas Hawkes Tanner, M.D., Assistant Physician for Diseases of Women and Children at King's College Hospital from 1860 to 1863, the sum of £200 Stock, for the purpose of founding a Prize in Obstetric Medicine.

1884. The Friends and former pupils of the Reverend Alfred Barry, D.D., D.C.L., Principal of King's College, London, 1868–83, the sum of £263, to found a Prize for Divinity in each department of the College and School, in recognition of the great services he rendered to the College.

1885. John Edward Rabbeth, the sum of £681 New South Wales 3½ per cent. Stock, for the purpose of founding an Annual Scholarship of the value of £20, in memory of his son Samuel Rabbeth, M.B. (Lond.), a former distinguished student of King's College School and Medical Department of King's College and a House Physician at King's in 1882, who sacrificed his life in an attempt to save a child who was dying from diphtheria.

1905. Sir John Phillips, M.D., F.K.C., one of the Editors and the Treasurer of King's College Hospital Reports, 1895–1903, by a benefaction relieved the Medical School of a financial responsibility.

1909. The Reverend Arthur Cayley Headlam, C.H., D.D., F.K.C., Principal of King's College, 1903–12, rendered especial services on behalf of the Medical School; he became Bishop of Gloucester in 1923.

1912. The Hon. William Frederick Danvers Smith (later Viscount Hambleden—the second), F.K.C., gave large sums of money for the advancement of King's College Hospital and the Medical School.

1914. Under the will of Professor Isaac Burney Yeo, M.D., F.K.C., the 'Burney Yeo' bequest Entrance Scholarships were endowed to commemorate his long connexion with King's College Hospital and the Medical School.

1916. Lieut.-Colonel J. M. E. and Mrs. Waddy presented to the Medical School the sum of £500 for the purpose of furnishing the Medical School library and for the erection of a tablet in memory of their son Lieut. J. R. Waddy, M.C., R.A.M.C., who was killed in action in 1915.

1916. Lady Worrell Carrington presented to the Medical School the sum of £200 for the purpose of furnishing the students' common room and for the erection of a tablet in memory of her son Lieut. Edward Worrell Carrington, M.C., R.A.M.C., who was killed in France, September 27, 1915.

1923. Frederic Francis Burghard, C.B., M.D., M.S., F.K.C., rendered especial service to the Medical School in the inauguration of the Clubs' and Societies' Union of which he was President, 1908–23, and was a generous subscriber to the War Memorial Pavilion Fund (see King's, p. 353).

1924. Sir Henry Cubitt Gooch and Lady Gooch founded the Raymond Gooch Scholarships in memory of their son John Wilfred Raymond Gooch who, when a schoolboy at Eton, died in September 1924.

1924. In memory of Henry Alfred Burridge, M.A., M.B., a former distinguished student of the Medical School and Lecturer in Forensic Medicine and Toxicology in K.C.H. Medical School, 1919–24, the Burridge Prize in Forensic Medicine and Toxicology was founded.

1926. In memory of Mrs. Jocelyn Johnston (née Almond), a former distinguished student of King's, the Jocelyn Almond Prize for research in Diseases of Children was founded.

1927. In fulfilment of the wishes of Charles Edward Wallis, M.R.C.S., L.D.S., Dental Surgeon at King's and Lecturer in Dental Surgery in the Medical School, his brother Mr. Ferdinand Wallis founded the C. E. Wallis Prize.

1928. Brigade-Surgeon Lieutenant-Colonel Albert Baird Seaman, I.M.S., a former distinguished student in the Medical School, established the Seaman Scholarship Fund for the sons of poor clergymen of the Church of England.

1929. To commemorate the life and work of Sir David Ferrier, M.D., LL.D., F.R.S., F.K.C., Emeritus Professor of Neurology in the Medical School and Consulting Physician to King's College Hospital, his friends and colleagues established the Ferrier Prize in Neurology.

1930. Thomas Percy Legg, C.M.G., M.S., Senior Surgeon of the Hospital and Lecturer in Surgery in the Medical School bequeathed £200 to provide two annual Prizes, one for Surgery and the other for Surgical Pathology and Morbid Anatomy. He bequeathed £100 to the Clubs' and Societies' Union. He also left the sum of £11,890 which eventually came to King's College Hospital Medical School.

1931. Mr. and Mrs. Frederick James Ware founded the Ware Prize in memory of their youngest son Norman James Ware, who died in his eighteenth year and was Second Boy of the Strand School, Brixton Hill.

1931. Arnold Danvers Power, F.K.C., Vice-President of the Hospital, presented large sums of money to the Medical School Centenary Building Fund.

1933. Colonel Sir Joseph Lister Cheyne, Bt., M.C., founded the Cheyne Surgery Prize in memory of his father Sir William Watson Cheyne, Bt., K.C.M.G., F.R.S., F.K.C., formerly Senior Surgeon of the Hospital and Professor of Clinical Surgery in the Medical School.

1934. Leedham Henry Fuller, M.R.C.S., a former distinguished student in the Medical School and one of the original founders in 1903 of King's College Hospital Masonic Lodge, left a large sum of money to the Centenary Building Fund for the Medical School.

1936. Lieut.-Colonel Ernest William White, C.B.E., M.B., formerly Professor of Psychological Medicine in the Medical School, left a legacy of £500 for the establishment of 'an annual prize in Psychological Medicine to be known as the Professor Ernest White Prize.'

1936. William Blair-Bell, M.D., F.K.C., a former distinguished student of the Medical School and later Professor of Obstetrics and Gynaecology in the University of Liverpool, left a legacy of £400 to provide a Prize in Gynaecology. Blair-Bell also left £250 to the Games Fund of King's College, London, for the purpose of providing prizes for the hurdle races and the open long-distance race or for an open boxing championship.

1937. Harold Waterlow Wiltshire, O.B.E., D.S.O., M.D., a former Consulting Physician to the Hospital, left the greater part of his property of the value of £22,481, subject to a life interest, to King's College Hospital Medical School.

1938. In memory of Professor Sir William J. R. Simpson, C.M.G., M.D., F.K.C., Lecturer in Tropical Medicine in the Medical School, 1918–27, a Prize in Tropical Diseases was founded by Mrs. Alec-Tweedie.

1939. The Trustees of Alexander Bohrmann contributed a considerable amount of money towards the cost of the new Dental Department of the Medical School.

1947. The Borland Scholarships for women were founded under the will of Francis James Borland and are intended to aid women medical students in their studies.

1948. The 'Cowburn Fund' for research in Pathology, Bacteriology, Morbid Anatomy, and allied subjects, was founded under the will of Surgeon Captain Arthur Douglas Cowburn, r.n.v.r., H.M. Coroner for the Southern District of the County of London.

1949. Charles William Menelaus Hope, o.b.e., m.d., a former Consulting Surgeon to the Ear, Nose, and Throat Department of the Hospital, left a large sum of money to King's College Hospital Medical School.

SECTION XVIII

AN EPITOME OF KING'S COLLEGE HOSPITAL AND KING'S COLLEGE HOSPITAL MEDICAL SCHOOL

KING'S COLLEGE, LONDON, was inaugurated in 1828 and founded by Royal Charter under the Patronage of King George IV on August 14, 1829.

The opening ceremony of the College took place on October 8, 1831, and lectures in the School of Medicine and Surgery—later the Medical Departments of the College—commenced on October 10.

The first King's College Hospital was established in Portugal Street, Lincoln's Inn Fields, in 1839, and it was laid down by the Council of King's College that the newly constituted Hospital was a public hospital for the relief of poor sick and infirm persons, and it was to be supported by voluntary contributions and to it the students of Medicine and Surgery belonging to King's College should, under proper regulations, for ever have access.

The Hospital was opened on April 15, 1840, and in order to preserve the connexion between the Hospital and King's College, the power nominating all Medical Officers of the Hospital and the Chaplain was vested in the Council of the College: the appointment of all other officers was vested in the Governors of the Hospital.

When the Hospital was first established it consisted of four departments—Medicine, Surgery, Diseases of Women and Children, and Dental Surgery.

The Royal Assent was given to an Act Incorporating the Governing Body of the Hospital in 1851.

The old workhouse of St. Clement Danes parish, which constituted the first King's College Hospital, was gradually demolished and a new Hospital was built, the foundation stone of which was laid in 1852.

The new Hospital contained a lying-in ward—the Nightingale Ward—a new feature in hospital organization, and the building was formally opened in 1861.

The Ophthalmic Department was established under John Soelberg Wells in 1865; the Laryngological Department under George Johnson, and the Dermatological Department under Alfred B. Duffin in 1867. The first anaesthetist, Hutchinson Royes Bell, was appointed in 1868. The Aural Department was founded under the direction of Urban Pritchard in 1876.

In 1885 Miss Katharine Monk was appointed Sister-Matron and a Training School for Nurses was founded; later a private nursing staff in connexion with the Hospital was established.

The Neurological Department was established under the direction of David Ferrier in 1889; the Laryngological Department was reorganized in 1893 and placed under the direction of Greville MacDonald.

In 1893 the Medical Department of King's College became the Faculty of Medicine of the College which included the Hospital.

The Electrical Department of the Hospital was inaugurated in 1899 and directed by W. Aldren Turner; in the same year the special department for Medical Diseases of Children was opened and placed under the direction of G. Frederic Still.

In 1900 the Radiological Department was instituted; F. Harrison Low was placed in charge.

In 1902 a Pathological Laboratory was opened at the Hospital under the charge of W. D'Este Emery.

In 1905 the Faculty of Medicine of King's College was divided into two sections: (1) The Medical Division of the Faculty of Science of which W. D. Halliburton was appointed Dean. (2) The Faculty of Medicine for Advanced Studies at the College and at the Hospital, of which Arthur Whitfield was appointed Dean.

Up to the year 1909 the government of the Medical School, which was then the Medical Faculty of King's College, and the election of the honorary medical staff of the Hospital had been carried out by the Council of King's College, London.

On the 'Appointed Day' September 1, 1909, the King's College London Transfer Act came into force, whereby King's College, London, including King's College for Women, became incorporated in the University of London and the Corporation of King's College Hospital became separated from that of King's College.

On the appointed day the Council of King's College, London, handed over the government of King's College Hospital to the Committee of Management of the Hospital which was then constituted a Statutory Committee.

To the Statutory Committee was entrusted the management of the Hospital and the government of King's College Hospital Medical School for advanced Medical Studies; under the Act King's College Hospital Medical School became constituted a School of Medicine in the University of London.

In the government of the Medical School the Committee of Management of the Hospital was assisted by three Statutory Committees or Boards: the Medical Board, the Medical School Committee, and the General Board of Teachers.

At this period Peyton T. B. Beale was Dean of King's College Hospital Medical School, and in 1910 Clifton Kelway was appointed Secretary to the Dean and to the three Statutory Boards.

In 1911 the Physiotherapeutic Department was inaugurated and E. Bellis Clayton became Director.

The Foundation Stone of the Hospital at Denmark Hill was laid by King Edward VII on July 20, 1909, and on July 26, 1913, the Hospital was inaugurated and declared open by King George V.

The Committee of Management of the second King's College Hospital in Portugal Street met for the last time in the Board Room of the Hospital on July 31, 1913; the Hon. W. F. D. Smith presided and the three medical members of the Committee present were Nestor Tirard, Albert Carless, and Willoughby Lyle (Dean).

The Hospital at Denmark Hill was opened for patients, and instruction commenced in the Medical School on October 13, 1913, and in that same year the first radiologist—Robert Knox was appointed.

When war broke out in August 1914 the larger portion of the Hospital was put at the service of the Government. A few wards were reserved for civilian and teaching purposes; the Casualty Department was used as an Out-patient Department and for 'casualties'. The portion of the Hospital used by the Military became the Fourth London General Hospital with Lieut.-Colonel Nestor Tirard in command.

In May 1918 women students were for the first time admitted as members of the Medical School.

In 1919 new Departments were established: the Cardiological under the direction of Harold W. Wiltshire, the Orthopaedic under H. A. Thomas Fairbank, and the Urological under John Thomson-Walker. An Out-patient Department for Psychological Medicine was inaugurated and placed under the direction of R. H. Steen, and the Department for Venereal Diseases was reorganized under Arthur Whitfield.

In 1923 the School for Dental Surgery was established and Alexander Livingston was appointed Director of Dental Studies.

In 1924 the Orthophonic Department was inaugurated and placed under the supervision of C. W. M. Hope and V. E. Negus, and in 1925 the Artificial Sunlight Department was established under the care of E. Bellis Clayton. In 1927 the Physiotherapeutic, Massage, and Electrical Departments became merged under the designation 'The Physical Treatment Department' under the direction of E. Bellis Clayton.

In 1927 the Lister Centenary Celebrations were held in the Hospital Medical School and elsewhere.

The 'Asthma Clinic' was inaugurated in 1929 under the direction of James L. Livingstone, and in 1930 the 'Rheumatic Clinic' was instituted.

In 1930 the Diabetic Out-patient Department was established, and two years later R. D. Lawrence was appointed in charge of it.

In 1932 the Departments of Oto-Rhinology and Rhino-Laryngology were amalgamated, C. W. M. Hope being Senior Surgeon. The Colonic Lavage Out-patient Department was opened in 1933 and treatments were carried out by Miss J. H. Chambers, a qualified nurse who had been trained at King's.

In 1937 the Stock Exchange Wing constituting the Private Patients Block was opened and in 1939 the new Dental Department on the ground floor of the Stock Exchange Wing was formally inaugurated.

A Thanksgiving Service on behalf of the Hospital was held in St. Paul's Cathedral in May 1939.

When war was declared in September 1939 the medical members of the Hospital staff were mobilized as members of the Emergency Medical Service for London. John B. Hunter was appointed Chief Medical Officer of Sector IX (King's College Hospital Sector) and Terence Cawthorne Deputy Chief Medical Officer, with headquarters at the Horton Emergency Hospital, Epsom. King's College Hospital was constituted a casualty clearing station with Bruce Pearson as Resident Physician and Harold C. Edwards as Resident Surgeon for a short time.

In 1948 the Royal Eye Hospital and the Belgrave Hospital for Children were amalgamated with King's, and in June Mary J. Wilmers was appointed Assistant Physician for Diseases of Children—the first occasion on which a woman was appointed a member of the honorary Hospital staff.

When the National Health Service was established in July 1948 the Hospital was taken over by the Minister of Health, who constituted a new board of governors for each of the London teaching hospitals. The Medical School became a 'Body Corporate' under the title of 'King's College Hospital Medical School (University of London)', and the government of the Medical School became vested in a newly constituted Council or Governing Body.

May King's College Hospital and King's College Hospital Medical School continue to carry on their arduous and responsible duties,

SANCTE ET SAPIENTER

INDEX OF NAMES

The principal page references are printed in heavy type.
Names which do not appear in this
index may be found in the lists commencing on pages 89 and 155.

INDEX OF REFERENCES

PRINTED IN
GREAT BRITAIN
AT THE
UNIVERSITY PRESS
OXFORD
BY
CHARLES BATEY
PRINTER
TO THE
UNIVERSITY